THE FURTHER CHRONICLES
OF
SHERLOCK HOLMES
VOLUME 1

DENIS O. SMITH

First edition published in 2018
© Copyright 2018
Denis O Smith

Paperback ISBN 978-1-78705-320-5
ePub ISBN 978-1-78705-321-2
PDF ISBN 978-1-78705-322-9

Published in the UK by MX Publishing
335 Princess Park Manor, Royal Drive,
London, N11 3GX
www.mxpublishing.co.uk

For Penny, Dorothy and, especially, Harriet, who have all, at various times, read and commented on previous collections of stories, in the hope that they will find something to enjoy in the present collection.

CONTENTS

THE FIVE KEYS

"BUT, MY DEAR FELLOW," said Sherlock Holmes, as we sat on either side of the hearth one morning after breakfast, "it is a question we have surely settled already!" It was a pleasant, sunny day in August, and we had been discussing the fascinating and unpredictable nature of the world. I had ventured the opinion that in the future the strangest and most surprising things were likely to be found in the unexplored jungles of Africa or South America, but at this suggestion my friend shook his head.

"The strangest and most surprising things are to be found right here in London, here and now in 1882," said he in a vehement tone. "It may be that you are less likely to be attacked by a crocodile in London, or to discover a previously unseen pink and blue parrot; but London is, *par excellence*, the haunt of mankind, the domain he has built for himself, and man is, as you can scarcely deny, the most complex and surprising creature on this earth. It is here that man weaves his webs of unpredictable action and reaction, here that he creates his puzzling riddles of behaviour. I am quite content to let others travel to the jungles you speak of, and chance, if they are lucky, upon their new parrots: for myself, seeking as I do all that is *outré*, all that is *recherché*, there is no field of enquiry so stimulating as present-day London.

"Just consider what is practically an everyday occurrence," he continued after a moment: "In one street a man is devising some scheme which he intends to shortly put into operation. It may be legal, it may be illegal; that is immaterial. Ten doors away, another man is devising a scheme of his own. These two men have passed in the street, but do not otherwise know each other, and neither knows that his own plans and schemes will be affected by those of the other. Three streets away lives a woman who has her own wishes and hopes, and who does not know either of the two men, but whose chance presence at a crucial moment will affect the plans of both of them. Each of these three bears a unique strand of life, and each strand is itself made up of an uncountable number of threads. When they meet, the strands become entangled and entwined, the threads merge in ways which are quite unexpected and could never have been predicted. It is then that I am consulted, to attempt to tease out the threads and make comprehensible what appears at first an utter confusion."

As he spoke, there came a sharp ring at the doorbell. I laughed. "Perhaps this is someone come to consult you about such a state of confusion," I remarked. "I think I shall withdraw and leave you to it."

"No, don't go, I pray you," returned my friend. "If it is indeed a client, I should like you to hear the description of the matter, and, if it isn't, we can continue our discussion."

I had risen from my chair, but paused at his entreaty, and a moment later a well-dressed, middle-aged man and woman were shown into the room and announced as Mr. and Mrs. Arthur Whitfield.

"What can we do for you?" asked Holmes as he ushered the visitors to the chairs by the hearth.

"I wish to retain your services for two days, Mr. Holmes, to act on my behalf," the woman responded in a business-like tone of voice.

"You see," said the man after clearing his throat, "my wife's uncle – that's my wife's father's brother – Ephraim Hardcastle – you might have heard of him – has recently died, and it is well-known that he was a man of some substance. He himself never married, and thus has no immediate heir. Under the circumstances–"

"Never mind all that, Arthur," his wife interrupted. "The simple fact is, Mr. Holmes, that Ephraim Hardcastle had five nieces and nephews, the sons and daughters of his brother and sister. These are his only heirs, of whom I am one. He died last week, and his will is to be read tomorrow. I wish you to be there."

"Are you unable to be present at the reading?" enquired Holmes.

"No, not at all," returned Mrs. Whitfield with emphasis. "I shall certainly be there."

"Then I don't understand what you wish me to do."

"I simply wish you to keep your eyes and ears open for anything underhand which may occur, and ensure that I am not cheated out of my rightful inheritance."

"I hesitate to disappoint you," said Holmes with a chuckle, "and I don't know what you have heard about me, but I have no formal legal training. It seems to me that if you wish someone to watch over your interests, you might do better to instruct a lawyer to act for you."

Mrs. Whitfield shook her head. "Not at all," said she. "I don't trust lawyers. They always have half an eye on lining their own pockets. In any case, it is not so much the possible legal issues which concern me as other things. I need someone I can trust to keep his eyes open and his wits about him, and I have heard that you are such a man."

"What, precisely, do you expect to happen?"

"I don't know. That is the trouble. If I knew what might happen, I should know what to do about it, but I don't. However, I strongly suspect that someone will attempt some chicanery, if they have not already done so."

"Whom do you suspect?" queried Holmes.

"Babbage," interposed Mrs. Whitfield's husband.

"It is not just Terence Babbage," said his wife quickly. "I dislike having to say it, but my own sister, Fulvia, is capable of acting in the strangest and most dishonest ways. She is very unworldly, you understand, and is the most unreliable person I have ever known."

"With the possible exception of Babbage," said Mr. Whitfield.

"One moment," interposed Holmes, taking a notebook and pencil from his pocket. "I cannot yet say if I will take your commission, but if I am to do so, I must have a clearer understanding of who is involved. Tell me, as briefly as possible, the names of all relevant people. Begin with Ephraim Hardcastle's generation."

"Very well," said Mrs. Whitfield. "There were three of them in the Hardcastle family: my father, Jacob, who was the oldest; his brother, Ephraim; and a daughter, my Aunt Miriam, who married a man called Gilbert Babbage. Is that clear?"

"Perfectly so. And the next generation?"

"My mother and father had three children, of whom I, Rosalind, am the oldest. I may be a Whitfield by marriage, but I am a Hardcastle by birth, and proud of it. Next is my younger sister, Fulvia, who has never married and devotes her time, in a half-hearted sort of way, to various charitable causes. Third is my younger brother, Anthony, who busies himself at the Commodities Exchange in the City. Don't ask me what he does there. I have asked him before, and I always find his explanations incomprehensible, but he makes a very good living out of it, anyway."

"Is he married?"

Mrs. Whitfield hesitated. "We thought he was. We had heard that he had married quietly somewhere, without telling anyone. We even met the girl – Gladys – a few times in Anthony's company at different functions. But now he never mentions her and it seems he was never married at all. Quite frankly, I was not sorry to hear that, as I had thought her quite unsuitable for him."

"So these three, Rosalind, Fulvia and Anthony are the three children of Jacob?"

"That is so. Jacob's brother, Ephraim, who has recently passed away, was the only one in the family who was really wealthy. He has no children – he never married – and was always known as something of an eccentric. He was certainly a miser, anyway. He amassed an enormous fortune in financial speculations, but never shared any of it with anyone else, spending his recent years cooped up alone with his money in a large house on the southern fringes of Brixton. His only interest, other than money, so far as I am aware, was in odd scientific experiments, concerning magnetism, electricity and the like, and he had a large room in the house converted into a laboratory so that he might indulge his interest whenever he wished."

"Did you ever pay him visits there?"

"Yes, occasionally. I would have gone there more often, but he always made it clear that he did not encourage visitors. On the odd occasions we did go to see him, he was never very welcoming. He would provide us with a cup of tea and a single biscuit and keep glancing at the clock as we spoke, as if waiting impatiently for us to leave."

"I see," said Holmes. "Now, did the third member of the Hardcastle family, your aunt, Miriam Babbage, have any children?"

"Yes, two: a daughter, Philomena, who is married to a publisher named George Gilpin, and a son, Terence, who is unmarried and is something of a dilettante in the world of art."

"So, let me see if I have got it clear: the five heirs to your late uncle's estate are yourself, Rosalind Whitfield; your sister and brother, Fulvia and Anthony Hardcastle; and, from the other branch of the family, Philomena Gilpin and Terence Babbage."

"That is correct."

"Have you any knowledge of the provisions your uncle's will might contain?"

"Not precisely, but it seems to be common knowledge that he has left everything he possessed to the five of us equally. How I know that, I can't remember, but I suppose it is from odd remarks made by my uncle himself, to me or to one of the others. Of course, there may be some specific bequests of which I am unaware, but I don't believe there will be anything significant of that nature."

Holmes nodded. "Can you give me the name of Ephraim Hardcastle's solicitor?" he asked after a moment.

"Certainly. It is Mr. Augustus Farjohn, of Welbeck, Lidgett and Farjohn, of Old Oak Chambers, in Fleet Street. As far as I am aware, my uncle had had the same solicitors for the last thirty-odd years. I have heard him speak very disparagingly of Mr. Farjohn, but I don't think he ever seriously contemplated moving his business elsewhere. Besides, my uncle was inclined to speak disparagingly of almost everyone who was not present. I don't doubt that he spoke that way about me when I was not there. He was an odd man in many ways, with a hard, sneering sort of manner and a distinctly unpleasant sense of humour. I don't think he had any friends – none, at least, that I was ever aware of."

"Is the will to be read at the house, or at Mr. Farjohn's chambers?"

"The latter, tomorrow morning at ten o'clock. Will you be there?"

Holmes nodded. "And my colleague here, Dr Watson. Have no fear, madam," he added quickly with a chuckle, as an expression of doubt crossed Mrs. Whitfield's features: "one fee will serve us both."

When our visitors had left us, I turned to Holmes in puzzlement.

"Of course, I don't mind at all accompanying you," I said, "but I am surprised at your accepting the commission, Holmes. It sounds to me a perfect example of the sort of thing you generally go to great pains to avoid: a case with no features of interest whatever!"

"That can scarcely be denied," returned my friend with a wry smile, "but you can never tell how things will turn out. It will at least be a novel experience, to learn how a miser leaves his money! Besides, I have nothing better to do tomorrow morning, and it should not occupy us for more than an hour or so, after which we can enjoy a stroll around Fleet Street and the Temple and perhaps, in celebration of gaining a professional fee for doing nothing, take lunch down there."

The remainder of that day passed uneventfully. About four o'clock in the afternoon, however, there came another ring at the bell, and a moment later a young woman was shown into our chambers and announced as Mrs. George Gilpin.

"I chanced to run across my cousin, Mrs. Whitfield, in Regent Street earlier today," she began when she had seated herself in a chair by the hearth. "Is it true that you have agreed to act for her at the reading of my late uncle's will tomorrow? You have?" she continued as Holmes nodded his head. "I might have known! Rosalind is always seeking to gain some financial advantage for herself, by any means she can."

Holmes shook his head. "I have no particular expertise in either financial or legal matters, so if your cousin somehow gains a pecuniary advantage over you or anyone else, it will certainly not be on my account. My brief, as I understand it, is simply to watch and see that everything is straightforward and above board. If any benefit results from my presence, which I rather doubt, it is just as likely to be for you as for Mrs. Whitfield."

Mrs. Gilpin rose to her feet, then hesitated.

"I wish I could believe you," said she.

"That is a judgment for you to make," returned Holmes. "I can only describe things as I see them."

"Very well," said our visitor, then, with a nod of the head and a rustle of her skirts, she left the room as hurriedly as she had entered.

"These cousins don't seem to trust each other very much," I remarked with a chuckle.

"Indeed," said my friend. "It will be interesting to see them all gathered together tomorrow. Perhaps they will come to blows and make what promised to be a singularly dull business a little more entertaining!"

At a few minutes before ten the following morning we reached the solicitor's chambers in Fleet Street, where a page showed us into an oak-panelled waiting-room. Mrs.

Whitfield and her husband were already there, and she introduced us to her sister, Fulvia Hardcastle, a somewhat untidy-looking woman who at once engaged me, in an indignant, heated manner, in a discussion of some government policy of which I knew nothing whatever. As we were speaking, our other visitor of the previous day, Mrs. Gilpin, was shown in, accompanied by a smartly dressed man whom I took to be her husband. A moment later, a formally attired elderly gentleman – evidently the solicitor – entered the room, rubbing his hands together and smiling at everyone in turn.

"Is everyone here who is coming?" he asked.

"Not yet, Mr. Farjohn," responded Mrs. Whitfield. "My brother, Anthony, has not yet arrived – I know he has been tremendously busy lately – and there has been no sign of Terence Babbage either, although that is not so surprising."

"And who are these gentlemen?" he enquired, turning to us. "Are they standing in for the absent relatives?"

Mrs. Whitfield shook her head. "This is Mr. Sherlock Holmes and Dr. Watson, who are here at my request, to act on my behalf if necessary."

"To act?" the solicitor queried in a tone of puzzlement. "In what sort of way?"

"In any way that seems appropriate."

Farjohn's eyebrows went up in surprise. "Their presence seems somewhat irregular," he murmured, "not to say superfluous, but I don't suppose–"

His reflections on the point were interrupted by the abrupt opening of the door, as a young man, somewhat dishevelled in appearance and breathing deeply, burst into the room.

"Sorry I'm late," he said in a breathless voice. "My train was held up for ages at Loughborough Junction."

"No matter, Mr. Babbage," said Farjohn. "Your cousin, Mr. Hardcastle, has still not arrived. Would anyone care for a cup of coffee while we are waiting?" he added, turning and addressing the others.

"Rather!" said Terence Babbage in an enthusiastic tone. "I haven't had a drop of nourishment since I got up this morning!"

"Perhaps you should have got out of bed a little earlier, then," said Mrs. Whitfield in an acid tone. "Really, Mr. Farjohn, I would much rather we got on with reading the will now. Perhaps the coffee could be brought into the reading-room. I'm sure that Anthony will be here any minute, and we can soon explain to him anything he has missed."

"Very well," said Farjohn. "If you will all follow me, I shall get everything ready."

The solicitor led the way along a narrow corridor and into another oak-panelled room. In the centre was a large, highly polished square table, around which were set a dozen or more chairs. Farjohn left the room, but returned in a few minutes with a large deed-box which he placed on the table before him. Opening the lid, he took out a folded and sealed document and five small, flat wooden boxes, each about six inches by two, by an inch deep. On one of the long, narrow sides of each box, I could see the outside edges of two little brass hinges, and, on the opposite side, a simple metal catch. By the catch, preventing the box-lid from being opened, was a large gout of red sealing-wax, impressed with some sort of design.

"Your uncle, Ephraim Hardcastle, has included a message for you all in his will," Farjohn began, as he broke the seal and unfolded the papers, "which I shall come to in a moment." He glanced round the table, cleared his throat and started to read. The last will and testament of Ephraim Joseph Hardcastle began in the usual, conventional way with a declaration by the testator that he was in sound mind and so on, then, after two legacies to domestic servants, which struck me as surprisingly generous for a supposed miser, he decreed that the remainder of his possessions, in whatever form they were, were to be divided equally between his five heirs, the sons and daughters of his brother, Jacob, and his sister, Miriam. At this news, there was a general murmur of satisfaction, and I heard someone remark that the will seemed unusually straightforward for something of Uncle Ephraim's devising. Farjohn held his hand up, to request silence.

"However," he said after a moment, "this division of your late uncle's worldly possessions is subject to the following provisions:

"'First,'" he continued, reading from the sheet in his hand, "'I have observed' – so says your uncle – 'that none of you appears able to get along harmoniously with any of the others. I have therefore arranged it so that unless you co-operate with each other, none of you will get anything at all, and you will regret it.

"'Second, I have sold all my stocks, shares, bonds and other securities, and have used the proceeds to buy precious stones, mainly diamonds. You will learn where these are if you follow the instructions I have given to Mr. Farjohn. These precious stones must be divided up into five equal shares. If any odd stones are left over after this division, they will be sold to a dealer by Mr. Farjohn, the proceeds of this sale being divided up five ways after Mr.

Farjohn has taken five per cent, as his commission for handling the transaction.

"'Third, several doors must be unlocked before you come to the precious stones, as you will see. For this purpose, you will each be issued with a key by Mr. Farjohn. Which key fits which lock you will not know until you try them. All the keys will be needed to gain your inheritance, and there is no advantage in possessing one key rather than another, so do try not to quarrel or come to blows over the issue. Be aware that there are no duplicate keys, so you must look after your key very carefully, or you will be unable to get past the doors. The builders who did the work for me provided me with two keys for each lock, but I took one set of these keys up to town with me some time ago and flung them into the Thames from the middle of Waterloo Bridge.'

"That is it," continued Farjohn after a moment, looking up and placing the sheet he had been reading from on the table, "saving only a note to state that if one of the five legatees is unable to be present at the reading of the will, then, with the approval of the other four, I am to act as agent for that person, hold in trust his or her share of the precious stones, and report back to him or her in due course. If, however, two or more legatees are absent, then we may not proceed at all – so it is fortunate that you arrived when you did, Mr. Babbage."

"What an absurd rigmarole!" cried Mrs. Whitfield.

"It does seem a trifle convoluted," murmured her husband to no one in particular.

"Oh, I don't know," said Terence Babbage. "For old Uncle Ephraim, with his odd way of thinking and odd way of doing things, it seems remarkably clear!"

"May I have a look at those little boxes?" asked Holmes, who had followed the proceedings without comment.

"Certainly, if you wish," returned Farjohn. "Ah! Here is the coffee! If anyone has any questions, please feel free to ask them!"

"These boxes, I take it, contain the keys," Holmes continued. "I note that they are not all the same weight."

"Indeed," responded Farjohn. "That is because the keys themselves are not all the same size."

"You were present when the keys were placed in the boxes and the boxes sealed?"

The solicitor nodded. "I then brought the boxes to my chambers here, where they were to be stored until required, in accordance with Mr. Hardcastle's wishes."

Their discussion was abruptly interrupted by a sharp female voice. "What is that man doing with those boxes? And what are they, anyway?"

I turned to see that Fulvia Hardcastle had risen to her feet and was gesticulating in Holmes's direction.

"These boxes contain the keys your late uncle referred to," said Holmes. "I am simply examining them. They are not marked distinctively in any way," he continued, turning to Farjohn, "so I take it they are to be distributed to the five named parties at random."

"That is correct," replied the solicitor. "It doesn't matter which box each person gets. Would you care to distribute them for me?"

"Certainly," said Holmes. He stood up, picked up the five little boxes, and was about to walk round the table with them when he was stopped by a sharp interjection from Philomena Gilpin.

"This doesn't seem right or proper," said she with a frown. "Mr. Holmes is acting as agent for Rosalind. Everyone knows that. So why should he be in charge of allocating the boxes to anyone? It should be done by someone with no interest in the matter."

"It really doesn't make any difference which key anyone has," said the solicitor. "However, if you insist upon the point, I shall find someone else to do it. Thelwell," he called to the youth who had brought in the tray of cups and saucers and had been busily pouring out the coffee, "leave that for the moment, will you, and hand out these boxes in random order, to Mrs. Whitfield, Miss Hardcastle, Mrs. Gilpin and Mr. Babbage. You'll have to give one to me, too, for the moment, as Anthony Hardcastle has not yet arrived."

"Very nicely made little boxes," remarked Babbage with a chuckle, as he turned his box over in his hands, "almost artistic in their own way. Are we supposed to open them now, or wait until Christmas?"

"You may open them whenever you please," said Farjohn. "When you have finished your coffee, we shall all go down to your late uncle's house to complete his instructions."

The seals were duly broken, the catches unfastened and the little boxes opened. Inside each of the boxes was a lining of green felt, upon which lay an old-fashioned iron key

"Why is my key smaller than all the others?" demanded Mrs. Whitfield of Farjohn, as she glanced round the table.

"It doesn't seem quite right," murmured her husband.

"I assure you it makes no difference to the outcome," said Farjohn in a tone which suggested he had just about had enough of the whole business.

"You should feel flattered, my dear Rosalind," remarked Babbage. "Your key is so much more delicate and lady-like than the others!"

Mrs. Whitfield appeared about to respond to this facetious comment, but in the end turned away, a look of distaste on her features, and drank her coffee in silence. At length, everyone had finished, and turned to the solicitor to see what was to happen next.

"We must now proceed to Mountsorrel House, your late uncle's residence, for the next stage of the matter," said he. "Mr. Hardcastle's old servants, Mr. and Mrs. Wilkinson, are still there, looking after things. Mr. Hardcastle gave them written permission to remain there until it has been decided what is to be done with the house. It is not far, so I think the easiest thing is if I get the commissionaire to call us, say, three cabs, and we make our way there that way."

As we filed from the room a few minutes later, Farjohn and I were the last to leave. He was picking up his papers and the key-boxes from the table when he abruptly paused.

"That is odd," said he.

"What is?" I asked.

"There were five little boxes here before, and now there are only four."

"Perhaps someone took one as a memento of the occasion," I suggested.

"Perhaps so," said he, nodding his head. "Well, well. It doesn't matter. They have served their purpose now."

Outside the solicitor's chambers, three cabs stood waiting for us in the street. Mrs. Whitfield, her husband and her sister, Fulvia, travelled in the first one, Mrs. Gilpin travelled in the second one with her husband and her brother, Terence, and Farjohn, Holmes and I took the third. We spoke but little as we made our way slowly through the crowded, dusty streets of south London. Holmes appeared to be turning something over in his mind, but what that might be, I could not begin to guess. It was certainly a singular expedition we were engaged upon, I reflected, and the terms of old Mr. Hardcastle's will were highly unusual. I found myself wondering, with heightened interest, what the legatees would be required to do with their keys when we reached Mountsorrel House, and I asked Farjohn if he had ever executed such an odd will before. He shook his head and declared that, in his long experience of such things, it was unique. I would have asked him other questions about unusual wills, but I could see that he was not inclined to discuss the matter further, so I was left to my own conjectures. There must, I thought, be some kind of safe or strong-room at Mountsorrel House, although why five keys should be required to open it, I could not imagine.

At length we pulled up at the gate of a large, gloomy-looking house, near the top of a steep hill. Within the gate was a very large garden, overgrown and unkempt, which surrounded the house on all sides. Away to the right, all along the far edge of the garden, stood a stone structure consisting of a row of pillars supporting a low, tiled roof, with a stone wall at the back of it and a long stone bench beneath, resembling nothing so much as the cloisters of a mediaeval monastery.

Farjohn led the way up the path to the front door of the house, where his brisk bang on the door-knocker was answered by an elderly, somewhat morose-looking man.

"Good morning, Wilkinson," said Farjohn. "We have come to fulfil the terms of Mr. Hardcastle's will."

"Yes, sir. I have been expecting you," responded Wilkinson, standing aside to let us enter. Within the house, all was silent and still, and there was a musty smell in the air.

"Now," said Farjohn. "Most of you are probably familiar with Ephraim Hardcastle's eccentric arrangements here, but I will just explain for those who are not. The structure you no doubt observed in the corner of the garden, with a row of pillars in front, was Mr. Hardcastle's summer-house, or part of it, at least. There is also an enclosed room there, at the left-hand end of the structure, where he sometimes took his meals, but when he was out there he spent most of his time just sitting on the stone seat which you probably saw behind the pillars. He liked to sit there and take the air whether the day was a sunny one or a rainy one. In fact, he particularly like sitting there when the weather was atrocious – he said the worse the weather, the more interesting he found it. He did not, however, like being out in such weather unprotected, and he had a positive mania about being watched or spied upon by what he termed over-curious neighbours or passers-by as he crossed from the house to the cloisters. He therefore had a long tunnel constructed under the lawn, so that he could pass from the one to the other without exposing himself to the elements or being observed by anyone. That may strike you as an expensive way to solve a slight problem, but that was his whim, and I suppose he had as much right as anyone else to spend his money as he saw fit."

Farjohn glanced round. "I don't know if any of you ever saw the inside of Mr., Hardcastle's tunnel, but he showed it to me shortly after it was built, when I visited him here about eight years ago, and I can tell you that it was very solidly constructed."

"He conducted me along it once in the middle of a thunderstorm, about five or six years ago," said Fulvia Hardcastle. "It was certainly a strange experience, to be so deep under the ground, and not one I particularly cared for."

Farjohn nodded. "I can understand that. More recently, when Mr. Hardcastle knew he did not have long to live, it occurred to him that his underground tunnel would be a secure place to store valuables, and, in particular, the precious stones he intended to leave to his heirs. He therefore had the far end of the tunnel, by the cloisters, blocked off completely, leaving a chamber under the middle of the lawn which is only accessible from this end. He also had a series of sturdy doors installed between the house and the underground chamber. It is these doors to which you have the keys."

"Where is the entrance to the tunnel?" asked Terence Babbage.

"I will show you," said Farjohn. "Follow me." He led the way along the hall, to a door beneath the staircase. "This is the cellar door, which is the way we must go. Be careful on the stone steps, which are a little uneven. Don't worry, Mrs. Whitfield," he added quickly, as she began to protest. "It is much lighter down there than most cellars are."

As we reached the foot of the cellar steps, the truth of the solicitor's observation became apparent. Large gratings, high in the side walls, admitted so much daylight that no artificial lights were required to see where we were going. I glanced at Holmes. He had been uncharacteristically taciturn throughout the morning's proceedings, and I wondered what he was making of it all. His features gave no clue to his thoughts, however, and, for all that I could tell, he might have been simply looking forward, as I was, to getting away from this odd assortment of people, returning to town, and finding somewhere to take lunch.

"This is the entrance to Mr. Hardcastle's tunnel," said Farjohn, indicating a stout wooden door a little to our left. As I looked closer, I saw that by the keyhole of the door, across the narrow gap between the door and the frame, a large gout of red wax was smeared, impressed with a seal of some kind. "I have been down here twice since the occasion I mentioned," Farjohn continued. "The first time was when he was having the underground chamber constructed, although the work was not quite finished then. The second time, more recently, was after Mr. Hardcastle had sealed these doors. That was the second-last occasion I ever saw him. He brought me here specifically to show me the seal on the door, and as he had already done it, this is as far as we went, so I don't know precisely what lies beyond this point, although I understand there are more doors."

"You say that that was the second-last time you saw him," said Holmes. "What, then was the last time?"

"When I came to collect the keys. I believe he had intended to give me the keys in their boxes on the occasion he showed me this door, but there had been some delay in the manufacture of the boxes and they were not ready. He therefore summoned me later to witness his sealing the keys in the boxes, after which I took the key-boxes away with me. That was the last time I saw him."

"Where had he been keeping the keys before he sealed them in the boxes?" asked Holmes.

"He had had them for some time on a cord round his neck."

"How dreadfully uncomfortable and inconvenient for him," remarked Fulvia Hardcastle.

"Never mind that," interrupted Mrs. Whitfield in an impatient tone. "How are we supposed to know which of our keys fits the lock?"

"I imagine," said Holmes, "that the idea is that you try each of them in turn until you find the right one."

"What an absurd waste of time it all is!"

"Look on the bright side, Rosalind," Mrs. Whitfield's husband interjected in a calm tone. "At least, with all these keys and seals involved, you can be absolutely certain that no one has forced his way in and stolen your inheritance."

"I should think not," replied Mrs. Whitfield shortly. "Try your key, Fulvia!"

Fulvia Hardcastle did as her sister had bidden her, but the key would not turn. Mrs. Gilpin then tried her key, but that, too, proved ineffective.

"Perhaps it is Anthony's key," said Mrs. Whitfield. "Have you brought that, Mr. Farjohn?"

"Yes," replied the solicitor. "It is here." But when he tried it in the lock, it would not turn even one degree.

Holmes chuckled. "The key you yourself are holding, Mrs. Whitfield, appears too small for that lock, so, by an admirable process of logical elimination, we have arrived at the truth: the correct key must be the one held by Mr. Babbage."

"What are you waiting for, Terence?" asked Mrs. Whitfield of her cousin. "For goodness's sake, don't keep us all hanging about!" she added in a sharp tone.

"I was just trying to remember," returned Babbage, "when it was that you were appointed senior overseer of this little enterprise."

"Now, now," murmured Mrs. Whitfield's husband.

"Someone has to take charge," retorted Mrs. Whitfield, "to prevent everything from descending into chaos. I'm sure that if Anthony were here, he would say the same. In fact, I'm sure if Anthony were here, he would naturally assume a position of authority. Some people have within them a natural sense of leadership and responsibility, which others can only envy."

"He certainly likes ordering other people about, as I have observed," remarked Babbage. "It's just a pity he's not quite responsible enough to show up at the reading of his uncle's will."

"At least he's made more of himself than certain other members of the family have," said Mrs. Whitfield in an angry voice. "I'm sure there is some very good reason for his absence today."

"Can we please just get on with it, and stop all this bickering," said Mrs. Gilpin. "It's giving me a headache."

Babbage put his key in the lock and turned it. There came the dull sound of the lock moving smoothly, and, when he pushed at the door, it opened easily. A hush fell on the cellar as we all craned forward to see what lay beyond the door, but it was very dark there, and I could make nothing out.

Holmes stepped forward, struck a match and lit a lantern which hung from a hook just inside the doorway. By this light we could see that beyond the doorway was a short flight of half a dozen steps leading down to a lower level. This was evidently the beginning of Ephraim Hardcastle's tunnel. It was about seven feet high and three feet wide, the walls and arched ceiling all lined neatly with bricks. Little of the tunnel was revealed, however, for less than ten feet further on was a second door, exactly like the one we had just opened.

"Let us see which key will open the second door," said Holmes, leading the way down the steps.

Fulvia Hardcastle pushed her way past him and tried her key in the lock. This time it turned easily, and she pushed open the door, to reveal more of the dark corridor. Another lantern hung on the wall there, which Holmes lit. As he did so, I saw that there was yet another door in the corridor, about a dozen feet further ahead. This third door, however, was somewhat different from the other two, and appeared even more impregnable. The whole front of the door was covered with what looked like a sheet of metal, in which there were not one but two keyholes, the one eighteen inches above the other.

"These keyholes look too large for your key, Mrs. Whitfield," said Holmes, "but you may as well try it. It's hard to tell sometimes from the outside how big a lock is."

"She did as he suggested, but failed to get anywhere with it. "I think, as you say, this key is too small." said she.

"This should be straightforward enough, then," said Mrs. Gilpin's husband. "There are two keyholes in the door, and only two keys left unused, my wife's and the one that Mr. Farjohn is holding for Anthony."

Farjohn tried his key in the upper keyhole, but reported that it would not turn at all. He then tried it in the lower keyhole, but with precisely the same result. "That's odd," he said. "Mrs. Gilpin's key must open both of these locks."

"It does seem a trifle pointless having two locks if the same key will open both of them," remarked Holmes, "but let us see."

Mrs. Gilpin tried her key in the lower lock, but could not turn it. Her husband then lent his strength to the task, but without effect. She then tried her key in the upper lock, and with a smooth click, it at once turned easily. "Now what do we do?" she said. "None of the keys will turn the lower lock, so we're stuck."

"*Nil desperandum,*" said Holmes with a chuckle. "Try your own key again in the lower lock, Mrs. Gilpin. It may be that turning the upper lock not only moves its own door-bolt, but also releases some impediment on the lower lock. Such interlocking devices are not unknown on strong-room doors."

She did as he suggested, but without success.

"If you would like to try your key again in the lower lock, Mr. Farjohn," said Holmes, "you might find that it now works."

"I follow your reasoning, Mr. Holmes; but if it does not work, then we are, as Mrs. Gilpin said, 'stuck'."

"Not necessarily," returned Holmes. "One of the keys left in the two previous doors might also fit this lock. But I think it most likely that the one you are holding will do the job."

Farjohn inserted his key in the lower lock, gave it a twist, and, with a satisfying, dull click, the lock moved.

Terence Babbage clapped his hands together. "There we are!" said he. "Undeniable progress!"

"I suppose," remarked Fulvia Hardcastle, "that this illustrates Uncle Ephraim's remark about co-operation being necessary in order to gain access to our inheritance."

"Indeed," said Holmes. "And as there is now only Mrs. Whitfield's key remaining, which is a different size from all the others and may open a chest or cupboard, I think your quest is almost over."

Mrs. Whitfield stepped forward and pushed at the door, which opened silently and smoothly. Beyond the doorway, as before, there was a hook on the wall, but this time no lantern was hanging there. By the dim light of the lantern behind us, however, I could see at once that beyond the double-locked door was not simply a continuation of the underground passage, but a much larger chamber altogether, about ten feet square. The walls of this chamber were completely covered with dark, glossy tiles which reflected the flickering light of the corridor lantern, and it was evident that this chamber marked the end of both the tunnel and the legatee's quest.

"I think there is another lamp hanging on the far wall," said Whitfield. "I'll light it. Yes, there is," he continued as he disappeared into the darkness of the room, but his voice broke off abruptly and there came a sudden shriek and a cry of pain.

"What is it, Arthur?" cried his wife. "What have you done?"

"I've fallen over something," Whitfield replied after a moment, a note of pain in his voice. "There's something like a heavy sack on the floor." There came a sudden point of light, as he struck a match, followed by a blood-chilling cry of horror. "It's not a sack," he cried. "It's a body!"

"A body?" returned his wife. "What sort of body?"

"A man's body. I think he's dead."

We all pressed forward to see. Holmes lit two further lanterns which Whitfield's match had revealed on the side-walls, and their flickering light revealed a ghastly scene. There, immediately beside a central table, lay the body of a man, stretched out face down on the stone floor. I quickly bent down to examine him, turning the head slightly and feeling the neck, which was as cold as ice. As I did so, there came a sudden ear-splitting cry of horror from behind me, which made my hair stand on end. "It's Anthony!" came Mrs. Whitfield's voice, then she burst into violent sobbing.

"Keep back!" said Holmes, who had been examining the table in the middle of the room. "Don't touch anything!" he added in a tone of authority. "There's something very strange here."

I rose to my feet and took a look at the table. On the top of it was a curious little tunnel-shaped structure, somewhat like a food cover, except that it was made of gilded wire mesh. On one side of it there appeared to be a lock with a small key-hole in it, and, at one end, a small handle such as that of a music-box or hurdy-gurdy. Beneath the wire mesh was a shallow white bowl, containing what looked like a large heap of precious stones. From the table-top, dark curtains hung down to the floor, completely concealing the space beneath. I bent to the body once more, as there came a babble of voices from behind me.

"How in God's name did Anthony get in here when all the doors were still locked and sealed?" cried Gilpin "It is impossible!"

"And what was he doing here?" cried his wife.

"More to the point," said Whitfield, "why is he dead?"

"If I didn't know it was impossible, ten feet below the ground," I responded as I examined the body further, "I should say he had been struck by lightning!"

There were cries of astonishment and ridicule all about me.

"But that is absurd!" cried Fulvia Hardcastle.

"How can you possibly suggest such a ridiculous thing?" demanded Babbage.

"There are no obvious wounds or marks of injury on the body," I began.

"Perhaps he was poisoned, then," interrupted Babbage, "or had a heart seizure."

"Perhaps," I returned, "but that would not account for this." I indicated the tips of the index finger and thumb of the dead man's right hand, which showed slight marks of burning. "Nor would it account for what appears to be damage to the inner ear," I continued, pointing to the small dried trickle of blood which was evident on the edge of his ear. "It also appears that he has broken or dislocated some vertebrae in his neck. All these symptoms are characteristic of having been struck by lightning."

"Are you an expert on the subject?" asked Babbage in surprise.

"I don't need to be. The symptoms of a lightning-strike are generally remembered by every junior medical student, as they are such an unusual and distinctive group." I unfastened the cuff on the right shirt-sleeve of the body and pushed the sleeve up a little way. "There," I said. "That settles the matter. That faint tree-like pattern of red lines you see there, beginning at the wrist and spreading out as it ascends the arm can be caused by nothing else but a massive charge of electricity passing through the body."

At this, there were further cries of astonishment, and, after the beginning of a scream, Mrs. Whitfield staggered backwards, almost insensible, and was only saved from slumping to the floor by Sherlock Holmes, who caught her as she fell. He handed over his limp charge to her husband, then turned to me.

"A very precise analysis, Watson, and exactly correct, of course, except for the small detail of the lightning strike, which did not exist."

"What, then?"

"A massive discharge of static electricity, every bit as deadly as a lightning strike. How long would you say he has been dead?"

"It is difficult to be precise. It is very cold down here, which would tend to slow down some of the post-mortem bodily changes, but taking all things into consideration, I should say he has been dead about two days, perhaps three."

Holmes nodded. "I agree."

"But," persisted Mrs. Gilpin in a tone of utter bafflement, "where did this supposed electricity come from?"

"From this," replied Holmes, drawing back fully the curtains beneath the table. On a lower shelf stood eight strange-looking large glass bottles, the outsides of which appeared to be coated with some kind of silvery substance. From the top of each of them, poking through the large cork which sealed the neck of each bottle, was a metal spike, and these metal spikes were all joined together by thick metal cross-pieces.

"What the devil are those things?" demanded Whitfield.

"They are Leyden Jars," said Holmes, "a device for accumulating and storing a large electrostatic charge. The shock from just one of those jars would probably be sufficient to fling you across the room. Linked together as they are by those copper rods, the charge would have been increased tremendously, and would certainly have been sufficient to give a fatal electric shock. If that were not deadly enough, there is also this little handle at the side of the cover over the gemstones, which presumably lifts the cover by means of the little gear wheels you can see; but it is also attached, by way of this band which passes through a slot in the table-top, to discs beneath the table. They are also geared, so that turning the handle even slowly will make the discs revolve at high speed."

"What would that achieve?" asked Babbage.

"It is, I believe, a miniature Holtz machine, another device for generating a huge electrostatic charge. This, as far as I can make out from the connections under the table, would feed into the Leyden Jars, which would store the charge."

"What!" cried Babbage. "You mean that that evil old devil, Hardcastle, lured us here with a promise of inheritance, only to try to murder us all?"

"I think that unlikely," returned Holmes with a shake of the head. "I imagine that his intention, however barbarously and maliciously conceived, was simply to protect that dish of gems from being stolen by an intruder. If his instructions had been strictly followed, and only those who were entitled to be here had entered, using the keys he provided, there would have been no danger. If you look at the bottom of the last door which we unlocked, you will see a flexible metal contact there which has rubbed along some metal strips on the floor, which are in turn connected by wires to this central table. I cannot pretend to understand all the complexity of what Ephraim Hardcastle has constructed here, but it is clear that the opening of the door has broken one contact and completed another, which has probably had the effect of conducting the electrostatic charge to earth and rendering this device safe."

"But what in Heaven's name are you saying?" demanded Fulvia Hardcastle. "You are implying that Anthony somehow got in here without unlocking and opening that door. That is utterly and completely impossible!"

Again Holmes shook his head. "That, I believe, is precisely what happened. Anthony Hardcastle did not come through the tunnel from the house as we did, but from the other direction, from the cloisters in the garden."

"But that, too, is impossible," protested Mrs. Gilpin, looking round the room. "There is no other door into this chamber but the one by which we entered. Apart from that one door, the walls are all completely solid and impenetrable. Besides, Mr. Farjohn has already told us that the far end of the tunnel has been blocked off."

"It's not true, though, is it, Mr. Farjohn?" said Holmes, turning to the solicitor. "No doubt there are doors built into the tunnel on that side – there must have always been at least one locked door – but I don't think the tunnel is entirely blocked off."

Farjohn stood in silence for a moment, a frown on his face, as if considering his reply. "I understood from Mr. Hardcastle that that was the case," he responded at length.

"I'm afraid I don't believe you," said Holmes. "On the contrary, I believe you reached a private agreement with Anthony Hardcastle to get in here before anyone else had a chance to do so and help yourself to some of the diamonds."

"How dare you!" cried Farjohn in an angry voice. "How dare you make such an outrageous accusation! And in the presence of such tragedy, too! I shall sue you for slander, sir, make no mistake! These people are my witnesses!"

"What's the idea, Mr. Holmes?" queried Babbage in a tone of puzzlement, a question which elicited murmurs of agreement from the others. "How can you possibly justify accusing Mr. Farjohn of having anything to do with this horrible business?"

"I make the accusation," replied Holmes, "because it is true. Mr. Farjohn is quite welcome to sue me for slander; I have no fear of that. The law holds that if the facts are true, no slander has occurred."

"But wait," interrupted Gilpin. "Perhaps Mr. Hardcastle's manservant, Wilkinson, let Anthony into the house, and so into the tunnel, and then, when Anthony was killed, returned the way he had come, sealing the doors as he went."

"No," said Holmes, with an emphatic shake of the head. "That really is impossible. I see no reason to doubt Mr. Farjohn's statement that Ephraim Hardcastle had kept the keys on a cord round his neck before they were sealed in their boxes, nor Hardcastle's own statement that he had thrown the duplicate keys into the river, in which case neither Wilkinson nor Anthony Hardcastle could ever have had access to any of the keys. Besides, all the doors we have passed through were sealed, and not recently, either. The surface appearance of sealing-wax alters slightly over time. I examined the seals, and it was clear to me from their dull and slightly dusty appearance that they had been placed on the doors some time ago. Anthony Hardcastle died about two or three days ago, whereas the seals have clearly been on the doors at least two weeks. It is therefore impossible that he could have come through the tunnel from the house as we have done. If we then dismiss entry from the house as impossible, what does that leave? It is an axiom of mine that when you have eliminated the impossible, whatever remains, however improbable, must be the truth. Anthony Hardcastle could not have come through the tunnel from the house; therefore he came through the tunnel from the cloisters. Coming that way, of course, especially if it were dark, he would avoid being seen by Wilkinson, and would only need one of the five keys, the small one now being held by Mrs. Whitfield. That, I take it, is the key to unlock that cover on the table. It was, I believe, when Anthony Hardcastle touched that key to the lock of the cover that he received the electric shock that killed him."

Mrs. Whitfield, who appeared to have recovered from her faint but was still leaning on her husband, looked down at the key in her hand, an expression of horror on her face.

"If what you say is true, Mr. Holmes," remarked her husband, "then how did Anthony manage to get hold of that key, which was being securely kept in Mr. Farjohn's chambers?"

"And how on earth," interrupted Gilpin, "do you suppose he passed through that solid, tiled wall behind you?"

"I take it there is a concealed door in that wall, directly opposite to the doorway through which we entered," said Holmes. "There must be – anything else is impossible – and I shall find it in a moment. As to how

Anthony got hold of the one key he required to get at the gems: he could only have got it from Mr. Farjohn, who was his partner in this enterprise."

"It's a lie!" cried Farjohn.

"I have mentioned," Holmes continued, ignoring the solicitor's outburst, "that I examined the wax seals on the doors and satisfied myself that they were several weeks old. I also noted that they were all marked with Ephraim Hardcastle's own personal seal, bearing the initials 'EJH'.

"What of it?" demanded Farjohn in an aggressive tone.

"Nothing. It was as one would expect. But the boxes containing the keys, although also sealed, were not stamped with the same seal, but with one which bore the image of a bird in a circle, with some smudged, indecipherable initials. What drew my attention to this when we were in your chambers, was that I also observed there the seal which had made that impression in the wax. It was hanging from your watch-chain, where I see it still. It is your seal, Farjohn, and you sealed those boxes yourself."

"Yes, of course, I do not deny it," returned Farjohn in a tone of annoyance; "but there is a perfectly simple explanation for that fact. I have mentioned that I had called here to see Mr. Hardcastle, when he showed me the first of the sealed doors to this tunnel, and I have also mentioned that the key-boxes were not then ready. He knew then that his end was not far off, and the unfinished business with the key-boxes was causing him great anxiety. He had been carrying the keys about with him for some time, as I mentioned. His fear, I believe, was that his manservant, Wilkinson, might enter the tunnel and steal the gems."

At this, Mrs. Gilpin interrupted in a sharp tone. "That does not seem either likely or fair," said she.

"Wilkinson is one of the most loyal servants one could imagine, and in the face of continual provocation from his master, too."

"Quite so," said Farjohn, "but your uncle was of a most suspicious and untrusting nature. Anyway, he sent a message for me to come and see him again a couple of weeks later, just a few days before he died. He was bedridden by then, and I attended him in his bed-chamber. Wilkinson brought in everything we needed on a tray, including the key-boxes and some sealing-wax, then left us. Hardcastle produced the keys themselves from under his pillow, where he had been hiding them. I put the five keys into the boxes at random, as he instructed me, and we sealed them up. However, he had misplaced his own seal, which could not be found anywhere, so he instructed me to impress the wax with my seal. That done, I carried the boxes back to my professional chambers, where they have remained ever since, until today. That is why the seal on the boxes is not the same as the seal on the doors."

"I congratulate you," said Holmes in a dry tone.

"What do you mean?"

"Your story is a very plausible one – although you have, of course, had some time to prepare it. Unfortunately, plausible or not, it is completely untrue."

There was an incoherent cry of rage from the solicitor, but Holmes ignored it. The others all fell silent as he continued:

"There are two points against your account. One is a matter of logic, the other a matter of observation. In the first place, regarding Hardcastle's supposed instruction to you to use your own seal to seal the boxes: that would be utterly pointless, and I don't believe for a moment that Hardcastle would have agreed to it. Once the boxes had been sealed, you were to keep them locked away in your chambers, and there would be thus no way that the legatees or anyone else outside of your chambers could get at them. The seals on the boxes were therefore not to prevent outsiders opening the boxes illicitly, but to prevent you or your colleagues at Old Oak Chambers from opening them."

"Preposterous!"

"There is no point your putting on a show of indignation at the suggestion, Mr. Farjohn. Such a precaution would not necessarily reflect personally upon you or your colleagues, but would be standard practice, as you are perfectly aware. In this particular case, however, there is a further reason why Hardcastle would take such a precaution. He was, as everyone agrees, and as you yourself remarked just a moment ago, a secretive and suspicious-minded man. If he could not even bring himself to trust his own loyal manservant, Wilkinson, then I very much doubt he would trust you. The suggestion that he would permit the boxes to be sealed by one of the very people he wished to prevent from opening them is ridiculous. As you possessed the seal, there would be nothing to prevent your breaking the wax seal on one of the boxes and opening it, then re-sealing it again later, which is precisely what I believe you did."

Farjohn's face had turned a white, sickly colour, but he said nothing.

"This brings me to my second point," continued Holmes. "I inspected the key-boxes when we were in your chambers, Farjohn, and I have brought one with me as evidence." He drew from his pocket one of the flat wooden boxes I had seen earlier. "This is the box which contained Mrs. Whitfield's key. It is clear from the most cursory inspection that this box has been sealed twice. The first lot of sealing-wax has been scraped off with a pen-knife, and later a second lot has been dripped onto the box and impressed with your seal. But this kind of red sealing-wax always seeps into wood a little and stains it. Scraping the wax off with a knife does not remove this stain, which is perfectly visible on this box where the second lot of wax has not quite covered the mark left by the first lot."

Holmes paused, but Farjohn made no reply, and there was a moment of utter silence in that strange underground chamber.

"You can't prove any of this," said the solicitor abruptly.

"We can perhaps settle the question of whether Hardcastle's seal really was lost by asking Wilkinson, who, as you stated, brought in the boxes and sealing-wax on a tray, the last time you saw his master."

Farjohn made a sudden movement, and in an instant he was holding a revolver in his hand, pointing it steadily at Holmes.

"You interfering busybody," he snarled, his voice full of hatred. "You clever devil! I knew you would be trouble the moment I saw you! What has any of this to do with you? Why don't you mind your own damned business?"

There was a slight movement from Terence Babbage, no more than a slight shuffling of his feet, but in an instant Farjohn had turned the revolver in his direction.

"Get back!" he cried, in a voice full of desperation. "All of you, get back! I'll use this pistol if I have to! Don't think I won't! Yes, I came in here with Anthony Hardcastle. I didn't want to. He forced me into it against my will. And I knew nothing of Ephraim Hardcastle's devilish man-trap there. If Anthony had not been such a stupid fool, he would still be alive now! He used to crow about how much money he could make from speculating on commodities; he didn't consider how much he could also lose."

"Is that what happened?" asked Mrs. Gilpin.

"Yes, and not just his own money, either, but many thousands of his clients' money."

"I always thought he was reckless," murmured Whitfield.

"When you say," queried Holmes, "that Anthony Hardcastle forced you into joining him in his attempted theft of those diamonds, do you mean he blackmailed you?"

"If you want to use that word, then yes. He claimed to have evidence that I had helped myself to old Mr. Hardcastle's money. Any defalcations of mine were utterly trivial and petty, I can tell you, compared to what Anthony had done with his clients' money, but he swore he would expose me if I did not do as he said and help him get at the diamonds. Anthony Hardcastle was a swine, a black-hearted swine! However, it makes no difference now," he continued after a moment. "I was intending to retire in a few weeks' time, anyway. I'll just bring my retirement forward a little. All my preparations have already been made. I am going where no one will find me." He backed away, towards the door, his pistol still pointing towards us. "By the time you raise the alarm, I shall be far away."

"Don't be a fool, Farjohn," cried Holmes. "Don't make matters worse. It's obvious what has happened here. No one will accuse you of causing Anthony Hardcastle's death."

"Perhaps not, but I have enough experience of legal proceedings to know that once they begin, things will get dragged out into the open which I would rather remained hidden."

As he spoke these last words, he stepped quickly through the doorway and pulled the door shut behind him. An instant later we heard a key turn in the lock. Babbage flung himself at the door, seized the handle and tried to pull it open, but to no avail.

"Careful of those metal strips on the floor," Holmes called to Babbage. "The whole thing may be deadly again now the door is closed. Everyone else keep away from the table."

Mrs. Whitfield let out a wail of despair. "What ever can we do?" she cried.

"We shall all be suffocated!" cried her sister, Fulvia.

"I think not," said Holmes, indicating a grating in the centre of the ceiling. "There appears to be a ventilator there, no doubt concealed above ground by the urn in the middle of the lawn. I shouldn't waste your energy on that door," he called to Terence Babbage, who was still pulling at the door-handle. Our best hope of getting out of here quickly is almost certainly to find the door hidden behind these tiles and make our way along to the cloisters."

"Why are you so sure that there is such a door?" demanded Babbage.

"I have explained my reasoning. There must be another door. My theory of the crime demands it. Nothing else makes sense." As he was speaking he had taken a pen-knife from his pocket and opened it. Now, with a glance at the door in the opposite wall, presumably to estimate the likely position of the concealed door, he began to stab the blade of the knife into the narrow spaces between the tiles.

After a minute of this probing, he stepped back with a cry of triumph, as one of the tiles swung abruptly open.

"It is hinged," said Holmes, "and was evidently held in place by some sort of sprung catch. And here, behind it, is a simple latch!"

He lifted the latch and pulled at it, and, with a creak, a whole section of the tiled wall swung open. Taking one of the lanterns from the chamber wall, he led the way along the dark corridor which was now revealed. About five-and-twenty feet along this tunnel, we came to a flight of stone steps, at the top of which was a stout wooden door. Holmes ran up the steps and seized hold of the door-handle.

"There is no lock on this door," said he over his shoulder, "but there are two large bolts, which appear to be pushed soundly home. Then how the deuce did Farjohn get out this way on the night he was here with Anthony Hardcastle? Ah, I see! The metal sockets into which the bolts are pushed have themselves been forcibly wrenched from the wooden door-frame. Entry was obviously gained to this tunnel by forcing open the door with a large metal lever of some kind. Of course, I should have expected it! They could not have had a key to this door. And the advantage of forcing the door open in this way is that it would at once suggest to the police that the robbery was the work of strangers, and no suspicion would attach to any member of the family. I admit that I had thought before that Farjohn and Hardcastle had intended to take just a few diamonds each, so that none of you would know that anyone had been here before you. But the way this door has been forced suggests to me now that they may have intended to take the lot, and leave the rest of you with nothing."

All the time he had been speaking, he had been trying to pull the door open, but it appeared to be jammed very tight. All at once, as he strained every sinew at the task, the door flew open, and as it did so a thin little piece of wood fell to the floor.

"Farjohn must have jammed that sliver of wood in there as he slammed the door, to hold it tight," said Holmes. "Let us now see where we have got to!" The others all seemed to be talking at once, evidently horrified at how close they had come to losing their inheritance entirely, but Holmes held up his hand. "There will be time for recriminations later," said he. "We must report what has happened to the proper authorities so they can get on Farjohn's trail without delay." So saying, he led the way through the doorway and into a light, airy room, where a table and several chairs were set out. Directly ahead of us was another door with a large glass panel in it, through which we could see the garden, bathed in sunlight. We passed through this second door, which was not locked, and found ourselves in the cloisters.

"What a blessed relief, to get out of that horrible, dark tunnel!" said Mrs. Whitfield.

"What do we do now?" asked Terence Babbage.

Holmes sat down on the stone bench and took out his pipe. "As I have been retained to keep an eye on everything pertaining to Ephraim Hardcastle's will, which, it seems to me, now includes both those diamonds down there and also the body of the unfortunate Anthony Hardcastle, I think I should remain on duty here. However, someone must notify the authorities at Brixton Police Station as soon as possible, so that they can put out an alert for Farjohn. Would you mind fulfilling that duty, Watson?"

"Not at all," I replied. "I know where the police station is, and it's not far from here."

"I'll come with you, to help explain it all," said Gilpin

"I was also going to suggest," said Holmes, as he began to fill his pipe, "that someone should tell Wilkinson what has happened, but here he comes across the lawn now, with a determined-looking step. It may be that he saw Farjohn coming up from the cellar and leaving the house in an almighty hurry, and is wondering what has been going on. Perhaps in return for a little enlightenment he will make us a pot of tea."

There is little more to tell of this strange affair of Ephraim Hardcastle's will and the five keys. Although Farjohn managed to elude the police for twenty-four hours, he was arrested the following day as he was attempting to board the continental boat train at Victoria station, and charged with conspiracy to commit theft. As he himself had predicted, numerous other facts emerged at the subsequent trial, concerning his dishonest handling of Ephraim Hardcastle's investments, which meant that Farjohn began his retirement with a spell at Portland Prison.

Three days after the events I have described above, we had another visit from Mr. Whitfield.

"I have a cheque for you, Mr. Holmes," said he, as he took a seat by the hearth. "I could, of course, have put it in the post, but I wanted to thank you in person for all that you and your colleague did for us the other day. Without your presence, your perceptive observations and your decisive actions, I dread to think what might have happened. Words alone cannot express the gratitude I feel, and the cheque is therefore for a significantly larger amount than your standard professional fee, but I hope you will accept it as a small token of my appreciation. I might add that my wife – though her pride may inhibit her from expressing such sentiments openly – feels exactly as I do, and specifically asked me to convey to you her immense gratitude."

"If you insist upon it," said Holmes with a smile, taking the offered cheque and glancing at it, "then I should certainly not be so rude as to refuse such a generous gesture."

We chatted for some time in a friendly fashion, reflecting on the strange and surprising events which had taken place at old Mr. Hardcastle's house, and after Whitfield had left us Holmes looked again at the cheque before passing it to me. It was at that time, I think, the largest fee he had ever received for his professional services. And yet, I could see from the look in his eyes that, notable though it was, the fee meant far less to him than the sincere expression of appreciation he had received from his client.

THE TREGORRAN HEIR

SHERLOCK HOLMES rarely showed much inclination to travel beyond the bounds of London. His preference, both professional and private, was to dwell in the midst of four million souls, and the countryside beyond the capital held little interest for him.

Nevertheless, it happened not infrequently, as his name became more widely known, that he was consulted by those whose lives were lived far from the bustle of the capital city, and cases took him, on occasion, to the most remote parts of the country. Among these cases were some of the most memorable I can recall, including the singular mystery concerning William Penney and the Knightsfleet Tower, and the strange and inexplicable disappearance of the Duke of Honingham, who was seen to enter the maze at Pomfrey Park in Hampshire one summer's evening, and was never seen again in this world. Perhaps the most remarkable such case, however, was that associated with the Tregorran family of Cornwall, and the mysterious and terrible events at Gipsies' Croft. It is this last case I shall now recount.

It was a wild and tempestuous day in the early spring, and we had taken breakfast to the beat of wind and rain against the windows. Afterwards, I had filled my pipe, and drawn my chair up to the fire, for the raw weather had caused my old wound to throb with a dull persistence. There, I had attempted to absorb myself in the morning papers, but they contained little of interest, and after a while my attention wandered and I found myself staring into the blazing fire and lamenting the dullness of my life.

"Perhaps you will find this a little more stimulating," said Sherlock Holmes, responding, as was his wont, to my unspoken thoughts. He passed me the letter he had been studying, which he had received by the first post that morning. It was addressed from Whitstock Farm in Cornwall, dated the previous day, and ran as follows:

DEAR MR. HOLMES, – I should greatly value your opinion on a proposal that has been put to me. You have, I know, succeeded in bringing light into the most perplexing of matters, and I hope that you may do so in my case also.

My home is at Fowey, on the south coast of Cornwall, where my father's family has for many generations been prominent among the fishing community. Recently, however, I have been approached by Mr. Michael Tregorran of Whitstock Farm, near Bude, who is one of the largest landed proprietors in the north of the county. He has no children, and proposes to name me as his heir if I agree to take his name. In accordance with his wishes, I have of late been residing with him, while I consider my decision.

It might appear that this proposed change in my circumstances is a very fortunate one; and it might be thought singularly ungrateful of me to have any reservations in the matter; but there are certain considerations which would, I imagine, make any man pause before agreeing to the proposal. It is commonly accepted in these parts that the Tregorran family has been dogged by ill-fortune for generations, and there are circumstances surrounding the family and their estate which cause me unease, and make me wonder whether it would perhaps be foolhardy of me to accept Tregorran's offer. Events this last week have only served to increase my concern. My benefactor wishes me to make a decision by the end of the month, so I have but a few days left in which to consider the matter. I therefore propose to call upon you tomorrow, when I can give you the details.

Yours sincerely, JOHN PENRYAN

"What a very strange communication!" I remarked, as I finished reading the letter. "I am surprised at your finding it of such interest, Holmes. The notion that a family might be 'dogged by ill-fortune for generations' surely belongs only in the pages of an eighteenth-century gothic romance!"

"And yet, there are possibilities," returned my companion in a thoughtful tone.

"Possibilities for people to let their imaginations run away with them, no doubt," I remarked.

"You do not recall the Tregorran murder case of three or four years ago?" queried Holmes. "No? Yet it occurred before you sailed for India, Watson. No doubt you were too immersed in your medical studies to notice such matters, but the case was certainly something of a sensation, and attracted considerable attention at the time. The most striking feature of the matter, as I recall it, was that the victim appeared to have been murdered twice."

"Whatever do you mean?"

"She had been throttled with great force, as evinced by the broken bones in her neck; but she had also been stabbed through the heart with some sharp implement."

"Good God!" I cried.

"I can give you the details if you wish."

My companion drew his own chair nearer to the fire as I nodded my head, and, after a moment, he continued:

"The Tregorrans were by all accounts a contented couple. They had no children, and lived a life of quiet rural seclusion, at Whitstock Farm. There appeared to be no particular anxiety in their lives. The husband occasionally hunted during the season, but had few other interests beyond the boundary of his farm, and, save an occasional visit to Bodmin, rarely travelled further than the few miles to Holsworthy, the nearest market town, to buy and sell stock. The wife was well known locally for the interest she took in the poor and the sick of the parish, and for the charitable work she engaged in with the wife of the local vicar.

"One foggy evening in the early spring she left Whitstock on foot, with the declared intention of walking the two miles to a neighbouring farm, where the farmer's wife was ill. The farm in question was on land owned by the Polcathro family. Now, the Tregorrans and the Polcathros, the two largest landowners in the district, had been engaged in a bitter legal dispute for many years, and, because of this, the woman's husband was against her going. According to the servants, the couple had words on the matter before she left. That was the last time she was seen alive. She never reached her intended destination, and her body was found the following morning in a remote part of the Tregorran estate near the coast, known as Gipsies' Croft. The question at once arose as to what had taken her to that part of the estate; for the natural route from Whitstock Farm to the homestead she had intended to visit was some miles inland of the spot where her body was found. No one could suggest any explanation for this.

When the district medical officer came to examine the body, he found, as I mentioned, that she appeared to have been murdered twice.

"At the inquest, the coroner queried whether the strangulation might not have simply rendered the woman unconscious, in which case the stabbing would have been the cause of death. The district medical officer, however, gave it as his opinion that the strangulation was so severe that it alone would have caused the woman's death, which, in his opinion, was what had happened."

"How did he explain the stabbing, then?"

"He couldn't."

"What a brutal and horrible affair!"

Holmes nodded. "As you will imagine, the case aroused enormous public interest. Extensive enquiries were made, both locally and further afield, but no facts were discovered which could shed any light on the matter. The husband himself was questioned at great length, but no charges were ever laid against him, nor against anyone else, and the case remains as puzzling now as it did then. You will perhaps appreciate, therefore," Holmes continued after a moment, "why my interest was aroused by Mr. Penryan's letter. Whether his account will add anything to our knowledge of the matter, we cannot tell, but I think we should hear what he has to say, however fancifully he might express himself."

John Penryan arrived that afternoon. He was a stockily built young man of about five-and-twenty, clean shaven and with thick black hair. He had the dark colouring of the Cornishman, with ruddy cheeks which bespoke a life lived in the fresh air of the countryside.

"It is not clear to me," said Holmes, when Penryan had recapitulated the contents of his letter, "why Michael Tregorran should have chosen you to be his heir."

"My mother is the younger sister of Tregorran's late wife," returned our visitor.

"The woman who was murdered?"

"Precisely. We were all greatly shocked by her death, which seemed so utterly inexplicable. Of course, in the district in which she lived, the tragedy was taken to be simply the latest manifestation of the Tregorran family's ill-fortune."

"Perhaps you could give us some details of the family and this supposed ill-fortune," said Holmes, leaning back in his chair and placing his finger-tips together.

"Certainly. Our families – the Penryans and the Tregorrans – have been linked for over thirty years, since the day that the two sisters, Hannah and Rebecca Tressillick from Lostwithiel, attended the county fair at Bodmin with their parents. There they happened to meet the two Tregorran brothers, Ulick and Michael. It was the older brother, Ulick, so I understand, who first caught Hannah's eye, with his loud, energetic manner, but as she came to know them better, she found Ulick's manner too wild and boisterous for her tastes, and her affections soon shifted to his quieter and more reserved younger brother, Michael, whom she married the following year. My own mother, Rebecca Tressillick, soon afterwards married Job Penryan of Fowey, who is my father.

"At the time of Michael Tregorran's marriage to Hannah, the young men's parents were still alive, and the whole family lived together in the great rambling farmhouse at Whitstock. It was in those days that Hannah first heard the old tale of the Tregorran Curse, which she subsequently related to my mother during a visit to Fowey. The story is soon told. It is said that two hundred years ago a family of tenant farmers on the Tregorran estate were cruelly and mercilessly evicted when illness had reduced them to poverty and they were unable to pay the rent. The tenant's wife, who claimed to be of Gipsy stock, pronounced a curse upon the Tregorran family and their estate as she was being driven from the land. There is a barren, rocky field on the extreme western edge of the estate which is popularly supposed to be the site of this event and is known as Gipsies' Croft. In a corner of this field is a ruined building which is said to have been where the evicted family had lived.

"The Tregorrans themselves utterly deny this story and say that not one word of it is true. They say it is a falsehood maliciously fabricated by the neighbouring Polcathro family, to blacken the Tregorran name. The Polcathro estate adjoins that of the Tregorrans, and the two families have been disputing the position of the boundary for a century or more. This quarrel is known throughout the whole of north Cornwall, for it has been pursued in the courts for generations, and is now, I understand, the longest-running case in Cornish legal history."

"Has Michael Tregorran ever spoken to you of this supposed curse?" asked Holmes.

Penryan shook his head. "He flatly refuses to do so, and became quite angry one evening when I raised the matter. My knowledge of it comes partly from my mother, and partly from a local source. Tregorran's own distaste for the subject is perhaps understandable, for there has been much tragedy in the family during his lifetime. Events occurred soon after his marriage to my aunt which destroyed the happiness with which they had begun their married life. His older brother, who was, as I remarked, of a wild, unrestrained temper, took to drink and quarrelled with everyone. Wilful and headstrong, he would never do anything which was asked of him, and was constantly in trouble. Eventually, when his dissolute life led to a period of confinement in Bodmin gaol, his father, Ezekiah, made a will leaving the estate to the younger son, Michael. Within six months of this will being made, Michael Tregorran and his wife were the only members of the family remaining alive.

"Old Ezekiah was found dead one evening in Gipsies' Croft, his skull fractured. His horse was wandering nearby, lame in the foreleg, and it was conjectured that the horse had stumbled over a rock and thrown his rider to the ground. Not long after this tragedy, the older son, Ulick, was journeying to Australia with a considerable sum of money, the intention being that he should study the novel methods of the sheep-farmers there, when the ship he was on was lost with all on board, off the west coast of Africa. These tragedies, coming so close together, affected old Mrs. Tregorran – Ezekiah's widow – very grievously. She fell ill, declined rapidly, and was dead within a month. Michael Tregorran and his wife, Hannah, were thus left alone to administer the cursed estate. Since that time there have been numerous minor misfortunes, which the local peasants were always ready to ascribe to the workings of the curse, but no serious incident until three years ago. Then, as you know, Tregorran's wife was murdered, in the most terrible and mysterious circumstances. That," said our visitor after a pause, "is the recent history of the Tregorran family and their curse."

"You said you had a local source for some of this information," observed Holmes. "Is that local source one of the neighbouring farmers?"

"No," replied Penryan with a shake of the head. "I have seen little of Tregorran's immediate neighbours during my time at Whitstock. Besides, although I have little doubt that they talk about these things among themselves, I doubt they would mention them in front of me. I have recently, however, made the acquaintance of two gentlemen who have a keen interest in these matters, although with widely differing interpretations. I will tell you how it came about. Several weeks ago, in early February, there was a local fair and ball at Bude. It is, I understand, an annual event at that time of the year, when the worst of winter is drawing to a close. Tregorran never attends, and although he did not positively prohibit me from going, it was clear that he would rather I did not. The last thing he said to me, as I left the house, was 'Remember, John, do not have anything to do with those bearing the Polcathro name. Avoid those devils as you would avoid the plague!'

"At the ball in the evening, which was held in the local church hall, my presence aroused a certain amount of curiosity. This was scarcely surprising, considering that I was a stranger to everyone there. Presently, as I ambled about, sipping from a glass of punch and listening to the very lively music, I was approached by a winsome and pretty young lady with very dark eyes, and dark curly hair which hung in ringlets about her temples.

"'Do excuse my boldness,' said she with a disarming little smile, 'but I don't believe we have been introduced.'

"'My name is John Penryan,' said I with a little bow.

"'Ah!' said she in a tone of recognition, 'the young man who is to inherit the Tregorran estate.'

"'Possibly,' said I. 'But how do you know about that?'

"'Oh, everyone knows about that,' she replied dismissively, with another arch little smile. 'Word gets around.'

"'And might I know whom I have the pleasure of addressing?'

"'They call me Catherine,' said she. 'How do you like the music, Mr. Penryan?'

"'I like the music very much,' I returned. 'Would you care to join in this next dance?'

"The young lady assented to this suggestion and we took our places in the long lines of men and women in the middle of the floor. As the band struck up a new melody and we whirled about, I was conscious that my partner scarcely ever took her eyes from my face, as if endeavouring to read the most secret depths of my character. It is an odd and disturbing feeling, to be the subject of such close scrutiny. I was conscious, too, that she had avoided – deliberately, so I judged – giving me her surname, and I wondered if the name she had failed to give me was in fact Polcathro.

"As the dance came to an end, we stood a moment recovering our breath, and then she began to ply me with questions, about myself and my situation. I had hoped that in the interval between the dances I should be able to learn something of her, but so rapidly did she question me, and so pressing was her manner, that by the time the music began for the next dance, she had learnt much about me and I had learnt nothing whatever about her.

"When our second dance ended, we were both out of breath, and I escorted her to the wooden chairs that lined the walls of the hall, where we sat down. As we did so, a young man approached. His appearance was so similar to that of my partner that I could only assume he was her brother. This assumption was confirmed by the familiar way in which he addressed her, as he asked her to introduce us.

"'This,' she answered him, 'is Mr. John Penryan of Whitstock, and this,' she continued, addressing me, 'is my brother, David Polcathro.'

"I nodded to him in what I thought was an agreeable way, but his only response was to stare blankly at me, in a way I found both rude and unpleasant. Then, without another word, he took his sister's hand, drew her to her feet and led her away. This, as you will imagine, I found a very unsettling experience, and it left me sitting all alone at the side of the room, feeling extremely self-conscious. Fortunately, my isolation did not last long. A few moments after Catherine Polcathro and her brother had left me, an elderly, white-haired gentleman approached and introduced himself as Edward Calvert.

"'Do you mind if I sit down here?' he asked.

"'Not at all,' I replied. I had heard that Calvert lived in the district, and knew him to be a retired professor from Oxford University, but I had never met him before.

"'You and I are perhaps the outsiders at this little festival,' he remarked, when I had explained who I was. 'As a matter of fact, I guessed who you were when I saw that young Polcathro boy acting so rudely towards you,' he continued, 'although I think his very charming sister may in fact be the more dangerous from your point of view, Mr. Penryan. Such young ladies have a way of using their charms for their own ends.'

"I nodded my understanding. Despite her prettiness, I had not been blind to a certain slyness and cunning in her manner.

"'But surely you are not still an outsider, Professor?' I said. 'I understood that you had lived in Bude for many years.'

"'That is true. I retired earlier than I might have done because of ill-health, and came to live in Cornwall because my doctor recommended the moist, mild climate. His advice was sound: within six months I was as healthy as I have ever been in my life, and have remained so ever since. But I have no roots here, no Cornish ancestors I can refer to in conversation, so, in the eyes of many – including the Polcathro family – I am still an outsider and will no doubt always remain so.'

"I asked him how he filled his days, for it was clear that, although advanced in years, he was still alert and lively in his thoughts.

"'As I had been professor of English and other literature in my Oxford days,' he replied, 'it seemed natural that in my retirement here, with time on my hands, I should turn my attention to the contribution of Cornwall to the body of English literature. I thought I should have my survey completed in three years or so, but three times three years have passed, and I am still working on it. In the last two or three years, I have moved on to Cornish folk-tales, the sort of things that are often not written down, but passed on orally from one generation to the next.'

"'Does that include the story of the Tregorran Curse?' I asked, at which he nodded his head.

"'Indeed,' said he. 'That is a fairly typical example of the sort of tale I am collecting. It is slow work, for it obliges me to travel all over the county. Not all the tales are as dark as the Tregorran story, but they often are, for, of course, the more dramatic a tale, the more likely it is to be remembered and passed on, sometimes with considerable embellishments!'

"I expressed my interest in the subject, and Professor Calvert invited me to call round and take supper with him one evening, when, he said, he would show me some of his research and we could discuss the matter further. His house stands on a headland just to the north of Bude and is very solidly built, to withstand the Atlantic gales which batter the coast there from time to time. I accepted his invitation with pleasure, and have dined with him there on three occasions. It has, I must say, been a great relief for me to get away from Whitstock Farm, even if only for a little while, and Professor Calvert's company is always both stimulating and entertaining, for he is a very learned man. His view of the 'Tregorran Curse' is that the tale was made up by some particularly imaginative story-teller, about a hundred and fifty years ago – he can find no earlier reference to it than that – to account for the poor and rocky terrain in the field now known as Gipsies' Croft. He informs me that such stories and legends, providing a dramatic explanation, of sorts, for perfectly natural – if unusual – features of the landscape are as old as civilization itself.

"On the last occasion I was at the professor's house, about two weeks ago, he had another guest to dinner, an elderly gentleman from Brazil. This was, therefore, yet another stranger to the district, and one who is, like the professor and myself, fascinated by the old traditions and legends which abound in Cornwall, which he has studied in some depth. He is certainly an odd, exotic character to find in such an out-of-the-way place. He is very large and exceedingly corpulent, and there is something quite imposing in his manner. He has a very large black moustache and swarthy skin, which is heavily lined from exposure to the sun. His yellowed, bloodshot eyes suggested chronic suffering from some tropical disease which is sapping his life away, and I noticed when he left us, to walk down the hill to his hotel, that he walked slowly and with some difficulty, leaning his weight upon a stout walking-stick.

"His name is Carlos Perreira, and he is a man of some wealth, being the owner of extensive coffee plantations in Brazil. I asked him what had brought him to such a remote spot, and he explained that several years ago, when he had been accompanying a cargo of coffee beans from Rio de Janeiro to London, a fierce storm in the English Channel had forced his ship to seek shelter in the Carrick Roads, off Falmouth. Laid up there for a couple of days, he had been attracted by the picturesque scenery, and had decided to explore the area, wandering on, as the whim took him, until he had eventually reached Bude. Enchanted by this charming little watering-place, he had vowed to return and spend a few weeks there each year, during the Brazilian summer. The tropical illnesses from which he has suffered have left him weak, he says, and he finds Rio unbearable during the hot months.

"When Professor Calvert was introducing us, Perreira smiled as he shook my hand. 'Your name is already known to me, Mr. Penryan,' said he, 'for you have been pointed out to me in the town as the man who is to inherit the Tregorran estate. You are aware, I take it, that it is said to be accursed?'

"I nodded. 'Professor Calvert and I have discussed the matter at length,' I replied. 'My view of it is much the same as his, that, interesting story though it is, there is no truth in it. Besides, I do not really believe in superstitious tales in general.'

"'Perhaps you are right not to do so,' said Perreira, 'but they are an interesting subject of study, nonetheless. There are many such traditions in my own country, and I have seen the effect they can have on the people there, and the countryside in which they live. Of course, the power of superstition is very much greater in Brazil than here in England. There, magic of all kinds is accepted without question by many peasants as an everyday fact of life, and such stories are believed implicitly. Who is to say if either view is entirely right or entirely wrong?

"'You and Professor Calvert are rationalists: you strive always to reduce the unknown to the known, the incomprehensible to the comprehensible. All well and good; that is your inclination. But what if there are some things which cannot be so reduced? After all, as your greatest poet says, through the mouth of Prince Hamlet, "There are more things in Heaven and Earth than are dreamt of" in the philosophy of a rationalist. There are many things we do not know, many questions to which no conclusive answer can be given. It is for this reason that I have taken an interest in the curse of the Tregorran family, and have made myself familiar with its history.'

"He discoursed at some length on the subject, comparing it with some very similar stories from his own country, and as it was apparent that he spoke with authority, I ventured to ask his opinion.

"'What do they say in your country about such curses?' I asked. 'Once pronounced, do they endure for ever, or is it possible that with time they may at last fade and pass away?'

"'Such things begin always with an evil deed,' replied Perreira after a moment, 'and until justice is restored the curse endures, like an open wound that will not heal. Then, one day, without warning, a fatal blow falls, and all is over – so!' As he spoke, he raised his hands above his head, then, with a sudden movement, brought them together with a loud clap. 'That,' said he, 'is my experience of such things.' And that, Mr. Holmes," said Penryan, "is the extent of my knowledge of the subject."

Sherlock Holmes sat in silent thought for some time, with his eyes closed. "And now," said he at length, opening his eyes, "the events of this week, if you please, Mr. Penryan. You remarked in your letter that something had occurred to cause you concern."

"That is so. I cannot pretend that my residence at Whitstock Farm has been an entirely enjoyable one, for an atmosphere of gloom pervades the place. Tregorran is a stern, reserved man, and is often uncommunicative for days on end. There have, however, been no incidents worth reporting, until Monday of this week. We were seated at the breakfast table, and I was reading a letter which I had received that morning from my mother. I was paying little attention to my host, who was glancing through his own post, when a slight cry, as of fear, made me look up sharply.

"At the other end of the table, Tregorran's eyes were wide with terror. His mouth hung open limply, and his face was as white as a sheet, as if every drop of blood had been drained from it. 'What is it?' I cried in alarm. His lips moved slightly, but no sound emerged. I dropped the letter I was reading, and sprang from my seat. In front of him upon the table lay a small brown-paper package he had opened. It contained nothing but a small quantity of children's bricks in a little cardboard box, of the sort which are decorated with letters of the alphabet and simple pictures of farm animals. It is no unusual thing for unsolicited articles to arrive in the post at Whitstock Farm – Tregorran frequently receives samples and testimonials from seed merchants and other such tradesmen – and I took it that this was something similar, incongruous though it seemed. But such thoughts were dashed from my mind as another inarticulate cry came from his lips, and he struggled to rise to his feet.

"He pushed back his chair, which fell over with a crash, and for a second swayed unsteadily on his feet, his fingers clutching at his throat. Then, before I could catch hold of him, he fell in a senseless heap to the floor. I rang for Lydford, his manservant, and between us we carried him to a couch and loosened his collar, for he seemed scarcely able to breathe. It was several minutes before he regained his senses, and then we helped him to his bed, where he stayed all that day. The following day he rose as usual, and made no allusion to what had happened. When I tried to raise the matter, he quickly changed the subject. It was then I resolved to seek your advice."

"You are quite certain it was the packet of bricks that disturbed him?" queried Holmes, a note of keen interest in his voice.

"Without a doubt. He had just opened it."

"There was no note in the package?"

"No."

"Did the letters on the bricks spell out any message?"

"Absolutely not. I looked to see. They were in a perfectly random order."

"Did you observe where the parcel had been posted?"

"At Bodmin Post Office."

"Has anything remotely similar occurred before?"

Penryan shook his head. "I questioned Lydford and the other servants on the matter, and they said they had never seen such a thing in all the years they had been there."

"Where is the parcel now?"

"I have no idea. Tregorran evidently instructed Lydford to dispose of it somewhere, for I have not seen it since the morning it arrived."

Again Holmes sat for some time in silence, his eyes closed and his brow furrowed with thought. At length he opened his eyes, an expression of decision upon his features, and addressed his visitor.

"These are deep waters," said he. "When do you propose to return to Cornwall?"

"By the nine o'clock train from Paddington, tomorrow morning."

"Then I shall accompany you. There is great danger at Whitstock Farm."

"Danger? For whom?"

"For whoever holds the Tregorran estate. Will you come with us, Watson?"

"Most certainly," said I, "if I can be of any assistance."

"My dear fellow!" cried Holmes, smiling. "You know how highly I value your presence! Until tomorrow morning, then, Mr. Penryan!"

We met at Paddington the following morning as we had arranged, and began our long journey to the West Country. At Exeter, we took a branch line which meandered across the moors, and shortly before four o'clock reached the little market town of Holsworthy. Penryan had wired ahead, and the farm trap was waiting for us. By it stood a ruddy-faced countryman in leather jacket and leggings, a downcast expression upon his face.

"What is it, Polford?" asked Penryan. "You appear troubled!"

"Mr. Tregorran has taken his own life," returned the other in a sombre tone.

"What!" cried Penryan in disbelief.

"He shot himself this morning," the man continued.

"Have the authorities been informed?" asked Holmes.

"The police are at the house now," returned the groom.

"Then we must get there without delay," cried Holmes, springing aboard the trap.

In a moment we were rattling off at a great pace down winding country lanes. Above us the clouds were low and dark, and a stiff wind was blowing. Holmes, I could see, was consumed with intense excitement and impatience, drumming his fingers upon his knee, biting his nails and consulting his watch every few minutes throughout the journey. But Whitstock Farm lay several miles distant from the town, and it was almost forty minutes before we turned in between the lichen-blotched stone gate-posts and saw before us the ancient grey-stone farmhouse, flanked by barns and other outbuildings.

As we alighted from the trap, the front door of the house opened, and a tall man dressed in a frogged jacket and braided cap emerged. He introduced himself as Inspector Culliemore, from the police station at Holsworthy, and upon learning Penryan's name, led us back into the house and along a dark, wood-panelled corridor to the study. In the centre of the room stood a large desk, covered with documents and slips of paper.

Sherlock Holmes handed his card to the policeman, who glanced at it for a moment. "I don't think we'll be needing any detectives here, consulting or otherwise," he remarked in a dismissive tone. "The facts appear very straightforward. Tregorran left home this morning at ten-thirty, carrying his shotgun. His housekeeper observed the gun, and assumed he intended to shoot crows. At about one o'clock, his body was found by a shepherd, in a remote part of the estate known as Gipsies' Croft. The police-station at Holsworthy was notified soon afterwards."

"Where is the body now?" Penryan enquired.

"It has been taken to Bodmin for further examination by the medical officer; although I doubt if he will have much to add to the opinion he has already expressed, that Tregorran died by his own hand, with his own shotgun. He took the full blast in the chest and neck, and must have died instantly."

"What makes you so sure it was suicide?" queried Holmes.

Inspector Culliemore looked round in surprise. "It is clear," said he, counting off the points upon his fingers. "He went out by himself with his gun. He did not tell anyone where he was going. He died by his own gun. There is no indication that anyone else was involved in any way. The servants all state that he had been in a grim, dark humour all this week. And, he left a note."

"May I see the note?" said Holmes.

"Certainly," replied the policeman. He picked up a sheet of note-paper from the desk and passed it to us. It was a plain white sheet, upon which was written: "Gipsies' Croft. Thursday. Eleven o'clock."

"A singular note," remarked Holmes.

"It appears," observed the policeman, "that he had already determined when and where he was going to end his life. That is not so strange as you might suppose. You may not be aware of it, but the place he chose was where his wife died, three years ago."

"I am aware of the significance of the place," returned Holmes. "This sheet has been folded in four at some time," he continued, as he examined the note carefully with the aid of his pocket lens. Where was it found?"

"On the desk," said Culliemore. "I observed the folding, and wondered at first if it had come in the post, although it did appear to be in Tregorran's own hand. But there is no envelope about anywhere, so I think it most likely that Tregorran made the note himself, to stiffen his resolve to go through with what he had planned, and folded it so that he could carry it about with him in his breast pocket. I have known suicides do such things before."

"No doubt," remarked Holmes. "Yet, in this case, he did not carry it with him in his breast pocket, or any other pocket, but left it here on the desk. If this note did come in the post," he continued, as he took the note to the window, with a couple of similar sheets of paper that he had picked up from the desk, "the envelope it came in may have been destroyed."

"His housekeeper says he received no post this morning," returned the policeman.

"And yesterday?"

"He received two letters. The envelopes were quite plain, and she does not know what was in them."

"Where are those envelopes?"

"Thrown away."

"Then one of them may have contained this sheet. Indeed, as the note specifies a day by name, it is more than likely that it did not arrive today but yesterday, or even the day before."

"Ah, Mr. London Detective!" returned the inspector in a tone of annoyance; "but you do not yet know all the facts! When I was questioning Tregorran's housekeeper about his recent mail, I showed her this note, and she instantly identified the hand as her master's. She says she is confident she could pick it out from a hundred such sheets!"

"Hum!" said Holmes, frowning as he replaced the papers on the desk. "That rather settles the matter, then. Would you mind showing us where the tragedy occurred?"

"I must return to the station, to write my report," replied Inspector Culliemore, shaking his head. "The groom will show you. He accompanied me when I first attended the scene of the death."

So it was that we climbed aboard the trap once more, and set off, by narrow lanes and cart-tracks, to the northern edge of the estate. The wind was very fierce now, blowing from the west, off the Atlantic, and whistling through the leafless wintry trees beside the road. At length the groom reined in the horse by an open gateway in a stunted hedge of thorn. "This is Gipsies' Croft," said he.

Through the gateway was a dismal, steeply sloping and barren-looking field. The lower end, to our left, appeared to be little more than bog and reeds, while the higher part, to which the groom led us, consisted of coarse grass and outcropping grey rocks, their surfaces blotched with moss and lichen. Ahead of us at the top of the field was a small ruined building. The two gable-ends were still standing, but the building between them had partly collapsed, so that, as we climbed the hill towards it, it appeared as a grim, horned silhouette against the leaden grey sky beyond. Before this gloomy structure, its fallen stones almost smothered by a tangled mass of brambles, our guide paused and indicated a spot on the ground where the bare mud had been churned up by the passage of many feet. On the nearest stones were dark splashes which were undoubtedly blood.

For a few moments, Holmes surveyed the ground, then he shook his head.

"A herd of buffalo could scarcely have done a better job of obliterating all significant traces," said he with a bitter sigh. "Still, that is as I expected. Let us take a look round the side of the building."

We followed him round the right-hand wall of the ruin, and watched as he examined the ground there carefully and then slowly made his way behind what remained of the rear wall.

"Ah! The cunning villain!" cried he all at once, pointing to a flat patch of bare mud, close beside the wall of the building. "See how he has sought to conceal the evidence of his presence!"

I looked closer, and saw that the surface of the mud, which I had taken at first to be perfectly featureless, was in fact marked by many shallow parallel lines. I was puzzled as to what might be the significance of this, until Holmes drew our attention to a clump of twigs which lay a few feet from the mud, and which had evidently been broken from a nearby tree.

"He has dragged this bunch of twigs back and forth across the mud to obliterate his footprints," said Holmes. "We must show that we are equal to his devilry! Is there any other way of reaching this field," he continued, addressing the groom, "other than the lane we took?"

"Yes, sir," returned the man, pointing to a gap in the hedge at the far side of the field: "through yonder gateway."

"Keep behind me," instructed Holmes, as he set off across the field, examining closely every patch of bare ground. "Ah!" said he at last, pausing before a broad swathe of mud which lay between two low clumps of grass. We leaned forward to see. In the centre of the flat mud was a small, perfectly circular hole, perhaps an inch across, and two inches deep. "Note that well," said Holmes, "for that marks the passage of this devil! He has stepped across the mud, from one side to the other, to avoid leaving a footprint, but it was a little wide for him."

"I do not understand!" cried Penryan in a tone of bewilderment. "I thought that you agreed with the inspector in the end, that Tregorran's death was suicide."

"Not at all," returned Holmes. "You evidently misunderstood. It is not suicide. It is cold-blooded murder!"

We hurried on, and passed through the gap in the hedge and down a short, steep track to a narrow lane. For several minutes, as the cold wind swirled about us, Holmes walked back and forth, examining the road surface and the grass verges at the side. Once he stooped, picked up a small object from the grass, and placed it carefully in an envelope which he took from his pocket.

"A pony and trap were drawn up here this morning for an hour and a quarter," said he at length. "The pony was tethered to a spike in the ground, on a rope six yards long. The extent of its grazing is quite clear," he added, by way of explanation, "and half-way between the two extreme points there is a small hole, indicating where the spike was pushed into the ground. Where does this lane lead to, Polford?"

"Up the hill will bring you to the Polcathro estate," replied the groom. "Down the other way, to the coast."

"Do you think you could manage to bring the trap across the field, to here?"

"I reckon so, sir," returned the man, and hurried off. Holmes took out his note-book, tore out a sheet, and scribbled a long note upon it. A minute or two later, the groom returned, leading the horse and trap, and Holmes handed him the note he had written.

"Make certain this message reaches Inspector Culliemore without delay," said he. "You will have to return to Whitstock on foot, I am afraid, Polford, for we must take the trap. We have no time to lose. Come!" he cried, springing up to the seat and taking the reins. Penryan and I clambered up beside him, he flicked the reins, and we set off at a brisk canter down the lane.

"Where are we going, Mr. Holmes?" asked Penryan.

"To Bude," returned Holmes. "We have failed to prevent the murder of Michael Tregorran. We must ensure at least that we bring his murderer to justice!"

"But who, then, is his murderer?"

"A man of very deep hatred and vindictiveness: your exotic friend, Senor Carlos Perreira."

"What!" cried Penryan in disbelief. "That cannot be true! Why on earth should Perreira murder Michael Tregorran?"

"Because Carlos Perreira is Ulick Tregorran."

Again Penryan cried loud in protest, and I, too, was stunned at this claim.

"But Ulick Tregorran has been dead for thirty years!" I protested. "The ship he was travelling on was lost off the coast of Africa!"

"He was only presumed dead," returned Holmes. "I rather fancy he had left the ship at Lisbon, and was thus not on board when it went down. We have heard that he was reluctant to ever do anything that was recommended to him. Perhaps he did not much care for the thought of Australia, and preferred to strike out in a direction of his own choosing. He had a considerable sum of money with him at the time, you will recall, no doubt sufficient to set himself up in whatever enterprise he wished. Probably he heard in Lisbon of the great financial potential of the coffee plantations, and took ship from Portugal to Brazil, where he appears to have prospered."

"But if he is still alive, why has he never made this fact known?" I protested.

"Why should he? There was nothing for him here. His younger brother, Michael, was in possession of all that might have been his: the Tregorran estate, and the woman, Hannah Tressillick. We heard how she had at first been attracted to the older brother, Ulick, but had subsequently switched her affections to the younger. This may have been of greater significance to Ulick than was generally appreciated. His opinion on the matter, after all, is not on record. I believe that for the last thirty years he has harboured the most intense hatred of both his brother and the woman who turned away from him, and has planned his vengeance carefully."

"You think he also murdered Tregorran's wife?" I queried, aghast at the horror of Holmes's theory.

"I am certain of it. No doubt he had made himself familiar with her movements, and waited for her in the lane near the farm on the night of her death. Perhaps he then identified himself to her, and persuaded her to take a stroll with him, until they were far from any homestead, and he had her at his mercy."

"Why murder her twice, as all the newspaper accounts reported?" asked Penryan, a look of horror upon his features.

"Who can say? Perhaps he simply wished to ensure that she was really dead. More likely, though, I believe, is that his stabbing her through the heart had a symbolic meaning for him, and represented his final triumph over her. You recoil with horror and disbelief at this suggestion, but if I am right, we are dealing with a quite exceptionally evil and determined man, who has spent thirty years in planning his terrible vengeance."

Holmes whipped the horse up, and we sped along the narrow lanes. We were close to the sea now, and off to our right we could hear the boom of the waves breaking upon the rocky coast, and see the sea-birds wheeling high in the sky above.

"It seems too fantastic to be true," remarked Penryan after a moment.

"It is the only hypothesis which will fit all the facts," Holmes responded. "I already considered it a possibility before we left London, and events since have only served to confirm it. You described to us how horror-stricken Michael Tregorran had been when he received the packet of children's bricks in the post. But why should that be? What could his reaction mean? It was clear from what you told us that Tregorran regarded the Polcathro family as his mortal enemies, but any communication from them would surely have been more likely to rouse anger in his breast than the dreadful shock and horror which so overcame him at the breakfast table on Monday. Clearly, for him, some great significance attached to this little toy. But what could that significance be? He and his wife had had no children of their own, and the domestic staff who had been at Whitstock for many years could shed no light on the matter.

"In the absence of any other explanation, I conjectured that the significance of this strange package might lie in some incident from Tregorran's own childhood. But why should this reminder of his childhood cause him such a terrible shock? Evidently the bricks conveyed to him some fact which was so utterly unforeseen and incredible that he was driven quite out of his senses. The likeliest answer, I considered, was that the bricks brought to his mind some incident – perhaps a childhood squabble he had had with his older brother – which only he and Ulick would know of. If that were so, then the bricks would at once convey to him that Ulick was still alive. This, I conjectured, might well have been sufficient to bring about his collapse. And if my hypothesis were correct, it also cast a little light on the mind of Ulick Tregorran, for it suggested that he remembered clearly some childish dispute of forty-odd years ago. Perhaps

Ulick's hatred of his brother had its origins in those distant days.

"When we arrived at Whitstock, and Inspector Culliemore showed us the supposed suicide note, it at once struck me that it might, rather, be a summons from Ulick Tregorran to his brother. The housekeeper had confidently identified the handwriting as her master's, so Culliemore concluded that Michael Tregorran had folded the paper himself, so that he might carry the note in his pocket. But it was evident to me, from a close examination of the paper, that it had never been in any pocket. The folded edges were not at all rubbed, and the rest of it was very smooth and uncreased. Furthermore, a comparison with the other sheets of white paper on the study desk showed that the folded sheet, although very similar, was in fact of different manufacture. I was therefore convinced that I was right, and that the message had arrived in the post, in an envelope which had subsequently been destroyed. But if that were the case, then the hand which had written it was not that of Michael Tregorran, and the housekeeper's identification of it as such could mean only one thing: that the note was written by Michael's brother, Ulick. As far as I was concerned, the housekeeper's testimony settled the matter beyond question. The study of handwriting is a fascinating one, which has not yet received the attention it deserves, although I have myself contributed one or two brief monographs to the literature. It is a singular fact that the handwriting of close relatives, even those whose lives have taken very different courses, is frequently so similar as to be practically indistinguishable.

"What I suggest happened this morning at Gipsies' Croft is that Ulick Tregorran arrived some time before the appointed hour, tethered his horse out of sight in the lane, and finished the cigar he was smoking, the end of which I found upon the grass there. Then he no doubt hid behind the ruined building until he heard his brother approach, when he emerged and took him by surprise. That Michael Tregorran had some notion of what was afoot, and expected trouble, is evident from the fact that he took his shotgun with him. How the older brother got this from him, we can only conjecture, but it is probable that Ulick himself was armed with a pistol. Perhaps there was some discussion between them, then Ulick discharged the shotgun at point-blank range, killing his brother instantly, and afterwards returned this way to Bude. During his passage across the field, careful though he was to leave no footprints, he inadvertently left the unmistakeable imprint of his walking-stick, as you saw. But, we approach Bude, where we must hope we can lay our hands on this cunning devil!"

We sped past a scattering of outlying houses, the clatter of our horse's hooves echoing back to us from their thick stone walls, then, as we rounded a bend, there on our right, spread out below us, was the vast expanse of the sea, leaden-coloured and rough, the rollers crashing and foaming on the beach far below. High above us, seagulls wheeled and soared, their blood-chilling shrieks seeming to echo the tenor of my own thoughts as Holmes finished his summary.

Penryan directed us to the Atlantic Hotel, high on a hill overlooking the sea, but there we met with a check. Senor Perreira, we were informed, had hired a carriage and left within the last hour for Holsworthy, intending to catch the seven o'clock train there, and make his way down to Plymouth, from where he sailed for Brazil in the morning.

Sherlock Holmes clapped his hand to his head. "Fool that I am!" cried he. "I should have foreseen this, for it was clear that his plans were reaching their climax!"

There was nothing to be done but follow our quarry to Holsworthy. We quickly secured a fresh horse, therefore, and set off in pursuit. Along the high road we flew at a tremendous pace, sending up clouds of dust in our wake, all the while straining our eyes to catch a glimpse of the carriage ahead of us. It was not until we were within a mile or two of Holsworthy, however, and the daylight was fading, that we hurtled round a bend in the road, our trap swaying wildly from side to side, and saw ahead of us two vehicles stationary in the middle of the road, with a number of men standing beside them. As we drew closer, I saw that the larger of the two vehicles was a police van.

"It is Culliemore!" cried Holmes. "Thank Heavens my message reached him! He and his men must have been coming from Holsworthy when they encountered Perreira's carriage."

We drew to a halt and sprang down. Inspector Culliemore was standing in the middle of the road, speaking to a very stout man in a large grey overcoat and wide-brimmed felt hat, who had his back to us.

"Ah! Mr. Holmes!" called out the policeman. "I got your note. But Mr. Perreira is very indignant at being delayed like this. Unless you can give me good cause to do otherwise, I shall have to let him go to catch his train."

Holmes did not reply to the policeman, but instead addressed the man in the grey overcoat. "Tregorran!" he called sharply as we approached, "Ulick Tregorran!"

The other turned his head abruptly, then, as if realising he had made an error, remained perfectly rigid, and glared at us. In that moment, his eyes met mine, and for an instant I had the awful, chilling sensation of gazing into the very soul of evil. Those hooded, bile-shot eyes seemed to blaze with malevolent fire from that dark, sallow face. Involuntarily, I stopped, as did Penryan. But Holmes stepped forward, and spoke again.

"Why did you murder her twice?" said he, in a matter-of-fact tone.

The other man's mouth opened slightly, his eyes flickered from side to side, then, with a sudden hoarse roar, he raised his stick and made to bring it down upon my friend's head.

It was the last thing he was ever to do in this world. Even as Holmes raised his arm to fend off the blow, and two police constables sprang forward to seize the assailant, he abruptly stopped. His fingers seemed to lose their grip upon the stick, which slipped from his grasp and clattered to the ground. For a moment, he clutched at his chest, his face contorted with pain, then, with a faint gasp, he collapsed heavily upon the dusty road.

I stepped forward, hastily loosened his collar, and examined him. It was evident he had suffered a massive heart seizure, and though I did all I could, it was to no avail. The man was dead.

Inspector Culliemore was not clear what part this Senor Perreira had played in the tragic events at Whitstock Farm, for Holmes's message to him had been of necessity very brief, but my friend soon apprised the policeman of his view of the matter. Then a discovery was made in the dead man's travelling trunk which cast a clear light on the case. Among numerous papers and documents was a thick diary, bound in red leather, in which Ulick Tregorran had recorded his thoughts over many years. Late into the evening we studied this dreadful volume, and read there of the evil pleasure he had taken in selecting the field known as Gipsies' Croft to be the scene of his terrible crimes. Of the murder of Hannah Tregorran, he had written as follows, in words which still make my blood run cold as I recall them: "Once this woman promised her heart to me. Then she gave it to another. So, now I destroy her heart. No one denies me with impunity!"

It also became clear from the account in the diary that Ulick Tregorran had murdered his own father when he learned that his father had willed the estate to his younger brother, afterwards beating his father's horse with a stick until he had lamed it, in order to conceal his terrible crime. It appeared, too, that his mother had suspected his involvement in the matter, which was the main reason she had sent him abroad. Holmes's conjecture that he had left the ship at Lisbon also proved an accurate one. From there he had travelled to Brazil, as Holmes had surmised, where he had remained for many years, until thoughts of further vengeance had brought him once more to these shores.

"I rather fancy," said Sherlock Holmes to me, as we returned to London the following morning on the Cornish Express, "that the death of Ulick Tregorran will mark the final act of the Tregorran Curse, which has cast such a blight upon the family and all those connected with it. Let us hope so, anyway, for it has certainly been a grim business. Now, Watson, I seem to recall that there is a concert of airs by Rossini at the Lyceum Theatre this evening. On the whole, my own taste is more for German music than Italian; but Rossini is light and cheerful, and an hour or two in his pleasant company may perhaps serve us as a suitable restorative!"

THE VICTORIA STREET MYSTERY

MY FRIEND, SHERLOCK HOLMES, the foremost criminal investigator in London, would sometimes expound upon the nature of his art. Although he would, at different times, address the matter in different ways, the general drift of his analysis was always largely the same.

"There are three principal factors in any successful criminal investigation," he would say. "The first is the training which the investigator has undergone, with regard to observation and deduction. This constitutes the foundation stones of the whole business, the *sine qua non* of the matter, without which the investigator must perforce rely simply on good fortune or the word of unreliable witnesses. The second is the experience he has gained from his previous investigations. This modifies and improves the accuracy of his observations and deductions. The third, which tends to be the least appreciated by the Scotland Yarders and the more sensational sections of the press, is the scientific outlook, which in practice means the keeping of an open mind. It is no use having had all the experience in the world if this very experience serves only to stifle and prejudice your logical faculties. Yes, we can say, the explanation which has proved correct a thousand times in the past may prove correct in the present instance, too, but it also may not. This cautionary principle must be borne in mind at all times, if you are to avoid falling into serious error."

This series of sketches in which I have attempted, however inadequately, to depict the varied career of Mr. Sherlock Holmes, has been designed to illustrate the points of theory which lay behind many of his cases. The third factor he listed in the remarks I have recorded above, concerning the importance of keeping an open mind when faced with apparently familiar facts, has never been better illustrated than in the case recorded in my notebook under the heading of "The Victoria Street Mystery," and it is this case I shall now recount.

One of Holmes's most frequent visitors, in the first year or two I shared chambers with him in Baker Street, was Inspector Lestrade, one of the senior detective officers of Scotland Yard, who would often consult my friend over difficulties he had encountered in his investigations. It came as no surprise, then, when, one foggy evening towards the end of November, 1882, a peal at our front doorbell was followed a few moments later by the appearance in our sitting-room of the keen-faced detective.

I rose from where I had been sitting beside the blazing fire.

"No doubt you would rather conduct your discussion in private," I began, but Lestrade waved me to my chair again.

"Not at all, Doctor," said he. "There is nothing especially confidential about the matter. Indeed, I would rather you remained. Your observations may prove invaluable, as they have on occasion in the past."

"I quite agree," said Holmes, ushering the policeman to his own chair by the fireside and drawing up the old basket-chair for himself. "A view from a different perspective is always interesting and sometimes enlightening. Now," he continued, turning to Lestrade, "what problem brings you to see us on such a cold and damp evening? I can see from your expression that there is something which puzzles you, but, unlike on some other occasions, it appears there is no great urgency attached to the matter. I surmise that your visit is not an official one, but undertaken purely on your own initiative."

"You are correct in every respect," returned the policeman in surprise, "but how do you know?"

"Had the matter been urgent, you would have taken a cab. Had your enquiry been an official one, you would also have taken a cab, and charged the fare to your employers. But I heard no cab before you rang at our bell and you have therefore come at least part of the way on foot. Your visit is therefore neither particularly urgent nor an official one. But I am sure that, for all that, it is an interesting one. You have our full attention!"

The policeman nodded his head. "It is a fairly straightforward business in most respects," he began, "but there are one or two points about it which are decidedly puzzling. In brief, the matter is this: there was a burglary at a warehouse down Shadwell way a few days ago, during which one of the thieves – a man who has already served time for burglary – was killed. It seems he must have had a confederate, but we can find no trace of this other man. It also seems that he had some connection with a very respectable address in the West End, but I cannot for the life of me think what that connection could possibly be. I have therefore come to you, Mr. Holmes, in the hope that you might be able to see some light in the matter where I cannot."

"Pray give us the details."

"It is soon told," responded Lestrade, taking out his note-book and turning the pages over. "Three nights ago – that is, on Monday evening – a constable – PC Dobbs of 'H' Division – was on his beat down Shadwell way when, as he passed along Dartmouth Street, about twenty past ten, he happened to notice a door ajar round the side of a warehouse, which he knew should have been locked up for the night. He therefore entered the building with his lantern in his hand. The place was in complete darkness and, as he cast his light about, he saw nothing to indicate that there was anything amiss. When he called out, however, there came an answering cry from the darkness, some distance away on the ground floor. He called again and got another answering cry, rather fainter than the first. Following the direction of these cries, he came at length upon a man – not anyone he knew – lying on his back on the hard floor.

"As he bent over him, Dobbs could see at once that the man was very seriously hurt. There was blood on the floor all around his head, and he seemed unable to move. Dobbs asked him what had happened, and, in answer, the man's eyes looked beyond Dobbs and upwards. Glancing up, Dobbs saw that some twenty feet above them was a metal walkway which connected with stairs from the ground floor to the upper floors, and it seemed clear that the injured man had fallen from there.

"Seeing that there was nothing he could do for him, Dobbs said he would go and bring a medical man, but before he left he asked the man what he was doing in the warehouse. To his surprise, the man abruptly raised his arm and, seizing the constable by the shoulder, pulled him closer and spoke in his ear.

"'Victoria Street,' he said in a weak, feeble voice. 'One-forty-one.'

"'One hundred and forty-one?' the constable queried.

"'Yes,' returned the man. 'Victoria Street.' Then he released his grip on the constable and put his hand up to his own throat where he seemed to be pulling at the scarf he was wearing. Dobbs carefully unfastened this and saw that behind it was a cord, tied loosely round the man's neck. The man put his hand on this cord and pulled at it, as he had done with the scarf, so Dobbs asked him if he wanted him to unfasten it.

"'Yes,' whispered the man. 'You take it.'

Dobbs unfastened the cord and pulled on it, drawing up from within the man's shirt a small soft leather pouch which was attached to the cord. He could feel there was some weight in the pouch, so he loosened the top and tipped the contents into his hand. To his surprise, he saw that there were ten gold sovereigns there.

Dobbs asked the man if the money was his, and, receiving a whispered assent, asked him what he wanted him to do with it.

"'Take it.'

"'Take it where?'

"'I've told you. One-forty-one.'

"'Victoria Street?'

"'Yes.'

"'I'll look after it for the moment, anyhow,' said Dobbs. He put the pouch of coins in his pocket and hurried off to get help. He says he was gone only about twenty minutes, but when he returned in a police-van, accompanied by the police-surgeon and two other men, the man in the warehouse had passed beyond all human help. The surgeon, who examined him more thoroughly later, says that he had undoubtedly fallen from a considerable height, as Dobbs had supposed, and in doing so had fractured his skull and several other bones. In his opinion, no one could have survived such a fall, and it was little short of a miracle that he had lasted long enough to speak to Dobbs as he had done."

"Is this constable, Dobbs, reliable?" asked Holmes.

"Absolutely," returned Lestrade. "He's very highly regarded. I would stake my life that his account is accurate."

"Has he been long in that district?"

"About three years, and on that particular beat for just over a year."

"But he did not recognize the man?"

"He said he thought he had seen him in the street a few times, late in the evening, probably returning home from some ale-house or other, but he did not know his name. As there was nothing on or about the dead man's person to indicate who he was, the authorities down there were stumped for a while. They called in Scotland Yard, and I went down there, but by the time I got there they had managed to identify him."

"Very well," said Holmes. "Pray continue."

"As you will no doubt be aware," said Lestrade, "establishing the identity of all the dead bodies that turn up in London is one of the most frequent and time-consuming tasks that fall to the lot of the police, and the men of 'H' Division soon applied their experience to the problem. One of the detective inspectors there, a smart officer by the name of Stanley, is a man after your own heart, Mr. Holmes. He examined the dead man's clothing and footwear, and observed that the little wedge of mud in the instep of his boot contained a considerable amount of sawdust. He speculated from this that the man had been employed in one of the timber-yards close by the river."

"Excellent!" cried Holmes.

"Yes, I thought you would appreciate the deduction, Mr. Holmes. Anyway, Inspector Stanley's surmise proved correct. After a few hours spent enquiring at every wood-yard in the district, it was established beyond doubt that the dead man was Alf Barnes, who had been employed at Chas Benson's timber-yard at Wapping. He had been in their employment for nearly two years, and had, they said, been a good reliable worker, never once failing to turn up for work until this week.

"Of course, once we knew the dead man's name, we were able to dig up a little more information about him. We discovered that about seven years ago, Barnes was arrested and charged with burglary from a warehouse near where he was found the other night. He was convicted and sentenced to five years' imprisonment, which he spent first in Pentonville and then in Wormwood Scrubs. At the time it was strongly suspected that he had been in league with two other men, Daniel Wolfe and Dick Cross, but nothing could be proved against either of them, so they were never charged. In fact, one of them, Wolfe, gave evidence against Barnes, stating that Barnes had tried unsuccessfully to persuade him to join him in his criminal activities. Barnes was therefore the only one who was convicted and sentenced. He was released from prison just over two years ago, and, after some time working as a casual labourer in the docks, got the job at Benson's wood-yard."

"What was it he stole seven years ago?" asked Holmes.

"Nothing very valuable," returned Lestrade. "He and whoever was in it with him were very much petty criminals. When caught he was attempting to make off with a cartload of stolen crockery – china plates and so on."

"Crockery?" I cried in surprise. "What a strange thing to steal. You wouldn't think it would be worth his while!"

"So you might think, Dr. Watson," remarked Lestrade with a chuckle, "but you would be surprised at the variety of goods that go missing all the time in the vicinity of the docks. The rule of thumb among some of the police officers down there is that if something can be stolen, then sooner or later it will be. From the point of view of these petty criminals, it's often not the stealing that's the difficult part, but the disposing of the stolen goods afterwards."

"Yes, I can see that that might prove difficult," I said. "How, for instance, would one go about disposing of a cart-load of stolen crockery?"

"That's something else you would be surprised about," replied Lestrade. "The truth is, there are always some shopkeepers, market-stall-holders and others who would think nothing of selling stolen goods if they thought they could get away with it and turn a penny by doing so. We know from experience that some of these crooked people even 'commission' the burglars to steal specific goods for them – things they know they will be able to sell. As it happens, I suspect that that is the case in the present instance."

"What was stolen on Monday night, then?" asked Holmes.

"Furs, Mr. Holmes, very valuable furs. The warehouse in question is one of those owned by a property company, Bailey Brothers. They have nothing of their own to store there, but let out parts of the building to other businesses by the week, month or longer. Most of the building is actually empty at present, but half of one of the upper floors is let out to a fur-importing business, J R. Rosenstiel, whose offices are on Cheapside. Their part of the warehouse is walled off from the rest of the building, and the door to it secured with padlocks. When my colleagues in 'H' Division inspected that door, however, on the night Barnes was found there, they discovered that it had been forced open and the padlock mountings wrenched from the wall. They summoned someone from Rosenstiel's who confirmed what they had suspected, that a considerable number of the furs had been stolen."

"That certainly suggests that Barnes had a confederate," said Holmes. "The missing furs were, I take it, nowhere to be found; Barnes did not have them; therefore someone else had already gone off with them."

"Quite right, Mr. Holmes. My own train of thought precisely. As to why Barnes's confederate had gone off and left him there, we can only guess. Perhaps the other man took the furs and Barnes was supposed to lock the place up and follow him, but fell from the metal walkway as he was coming downstairs. Perhaps Barnes had his accident while the other man was still there, and the other thought he was dead, or close to it, and decided to abandon him. Or perhaps it wasn't an accident at all: perhaps Barnes and his confederate quarrelled about something and had a fight on the walkway, during which Barnes fell – or was pushed – off it. We've no way of knowing what happened. Besides, there's little point in thinking about it at the moment, as we have no idea who Barnes was working with. He seems to have lived a very solitary life since he came out of prison, and doesn't appear to have had any friends at all. The only acquaintance of his that we've managed to find is a neighbour in Beckman Street, which is where he lived, a man by the name of John Gilbert. He's a respectable man with a wife and family, who has a senior job in the docks which he's had for nearly twenty years. He's just the sort of man whose testimony you feel you can rely on, and he says that Barnes lived alone, always kept himself to himself and never had any visitors. As far as Gilbert is aware, Barnes never spoke to anybody other than Gilbert himself and the man at the corner shop."

"What about those men who were suspected of having been involved with Barnes in the earlier robbery?" asked Holmes.

"What, Wolfe and Cross? There's nothing there, as far as I can see, Mr. Holmes. Barnes fell out with them completely when he went to prison – not surprising, really, considering they'd given evidence against him – and, so far as I've been able to discover, he's never spoken a word to them since. I can't find a single person who has ever seen them together since Barnes came out of the Scrubs, two years ago."

"Did you question PC Dobbs as to whether he had seen anyone in the nearby streets before he found Barnes?" asked Holmes.

"I certainly did," replied Lestrade. "He said the only people he saw were two men and a lad on a builder's cart, a few minutes before he turned into Dartmouth Street. He says they didn't seem to be in any particular hurry. He spoke to them and they told him they had been working late to finish a special job. He had a look in the back of the cart as they passed him, but says that all he could see there were a couple of planks of wood, a lot of timber off-cuts, a pile of house-bricks and some sacks of sand and cement."

"Did he recognize the men?"

"No."

"Was there any name displayed on the cart?"

Lestrade shook his head. "I specifically asked him that, but he said not. It would therefore be the very devil to find that cart now – and, of course, it's probably got nothing whatever to do with the crime, anyway. It is for that reason that I have been trying to approach the problem from the other end, as it were, that is, by investigating the Victoria Street connection. Unfortunately, I've not yet had any success there, which is what brings me here tonight."

"What do you mean?" I asked.

"I mentioned to you that just as important for these petty criminals as the theft itself is to find a way of disposing profitably of their plunder. I also mentioned that sometimes such thefts were 'commissioned' by those who were hoping to sell the stolen goods. With this in mind, I wondered if Barnes's repeated references to the address in Victoria Street might not provide us with a clue in that direction. I know, of course, that this sounds absurd: Victoria Street is one of the finest modern streets in the whole of London. It lies in the very heart of Westminster, with the Houses of Parliament and Westminster Abbey at one end and Victoria station at the other, and with fine new shops and offices in between. You simply cannot find anywhere more solid and respectable, and I am sure that most of the businesses in a street like that are of the very highest probity. But, as I know from my twenty years on the force, you can never tell for certain: sometimes you come across a cunning, plausible villain mingling with the most decent and honest folk you could imagine.

"I have therefore been making discreet enquiries about the address Barnes gave to PC Dobbs, one hundred and forty-one Victoria Street. It is one of those solid but somewhat anonymous buildings which have sprung up in that street in recent years. The owners are a firm called Westminster Commercial Properties Ltd, of which the chairman and largest shareholder is Lord Westfield. I can't think that there is anything suspicious there. The building itself is let out in six separate lots, one of which is vacant at the moment. I'll tell you who the five present tenants are."

Lestrade turned another page in his note-book, and read out a list he had made there: "First," he began, "there is the St Thomas Missionary Society, which, as the name suggests, is a charitable organization, which collects donations and pays for missionaries in parts of Africa and India. Second, W. P. Walker & Son, civil engineers. Third, the London and Moscow Importing Company – they specialize in Russian pictures, jewellery and other trinkets. Fourth, Snelgrove and Company, house and estate agents. Fifth, Nelson and Newsome, timber importers – they deal largely with the Scandinavian countries, so I understand." The policeman paused, a wry expression on his face. "And that, I'm afraid, is that," said he. "Not very promising, is it! Have you ever had any reason to come across any of these people, Mr. Holmes?"

"I don't believe so," replied my friend with a frown. He stood up and selected a couple of volumes from the long shelf of commonplace books in which he pasted newspaper cuttings on any subject which struck him as interesting. "No, there's no reference here to any of those people," he remarked as he turned the pages over rapidly.

"Is it possible," I asked Lestrade, "that there is another Victoria Street somewhere in London to which Barnes might have been referring?"

The policeman shook his head. "I've looked into that possibility already, Dr. Watson, and it's no use. Save only a short street in Greenwich, there is no other."

"As civil engineers sell only their expertise and mathematical calculations," I remarked, "and can have no use for furs, W. P. Walker & Son can surely be ruled out."

"Indeed," said Lestrade, "and, for similar reasons, the housing agents, Snelgrove & Co, can certainly be dismissed from consideration. The missionary society, too, has obviously nothing to do with any criminal enterprise, which leaves us with only the two importing companies, the one of Scandinavian timber and the other of Russian art and trinkets. Neither seems to have anything to do with furs, but it is an odd chance that the northern territories of both places – Russia and Scandinavia – are known for hunting and trapping, and I imagine a lot of furs do come from there."

"That is true," I remarked. "But I have been wondering about the missionary society, Lestrade. Not that there might be anything criminal about it, of course, but I wonder if Barnes might have been telling PC Dobbs that he wished to donate the money in his purse to it. He certainly made a point of drawing Dobbs's notice to the purse he was carrying."

"I suppose that what you suggest might be possible in theory, Dr. Watson, and there is, as they say, 'always a first time' for everything, but I can't really see a criminal like Alf Barnes thinking of contributing to a missionary society – and with such a large sum as ten pounds, too. If you'd brushed up against these villains as much as I have over the years, I think you'd agree with me."

"Perhaps you're right," I conceded. "But there is another possibility: perhaps one of the businesses at that address in Victoria Street was robbed by Barnes on some previous occasion, and in a fit of remorse he wished to make restitution to them for it."

"I should say the same applies to that suggestion as to your other one," responded Lestrade in a dismissive tone. "I just can't see one of these petty criminals thinking that way. In any case, it would be a deuced funny thing to have remorse for an old crime while busily engaged in a new one! What do you think, Mr. Holmes?"

Sherlock Holmes frowned. He had taken a street-map of London from the shelf as we had been speaking, and was studying it intently in silence. "Did you say that Barnes's home address was in Beckman Street?" he asked the policeman at length.

Lestrade consulted his notebook. "Yes, number thirteen," he replied. "Beckman Street is near the south end of Montgomery Road."

"I see it," said Holmes, eyeing the map closely. "And the address of Benson's timber-yard?"

"Upton Street, close by the river, in Wapping."

"Hum!" said Holmes, who appeared to be deep in thought. "I can't help feeling that there is something suggestive about all this! I think, Lestrade," he continued after a long moment of silence, "that, if you wish it, I shall look into the matter for you tomorrow."

"I should be very pleased if you would," returned the policeman.

"In that case," said Holmes, "I should be obliged if you could let me have a signed authority, so that there will be no difficulty about my viewing the body, borrowing Barnes's house-key for a little while and so on."

"Certainly," said Lestrade, taking a folded slip of paper from his inside pocket. "I have a suitable form here which I shall just fill in and sign. But, if I may say so, I don't think you will discover anything fresh in the East End, Mr. Holmes. I think that, between the two of us, Inspector Stanley and I have examined every possible aspect of the case in those parts without turning up anything of value. It is for that very reason, as I have explained, that I have been concentrating my efforts today on the possible West End connections of the matter, which I shall continue tomorrow."

Holmes nodded, a smile on his face. "I understand," said he. "I am sure that you and Stanley have done as thorough a job as you can, Lestrade. But you know my methods: I like to start afresh at the beginning of a case and see everything for myself, even if it is exactly the same as a hundred other people have already seen!"

The following morning Holmes had risen early and left the house before I descended for breakfast. Leaning up against the marmalade-pot, however, was a note he had left me, which ran as follows:

I know you take an interest in my cases, Watson, so here is something for you to consider concerning the present business. On the chemical bench you will see the street-map of London, folded to show the East End. I have marked three places with little pieces of a broken matchstick. See what you make of it. When I return we can compare our conclusions on the matter.
– S. H.

I crossed to Holmes's chemical bench and examined the map. One piece of the matchstick was placed on Upton Street, in Wapping, close to the river. That, I remembered, was the address of the timber-yard at which Barnes had been employed. The next piece of the matchstick lay on Dartmouth Street, which ran approximately south to north, towards the Commercial Road, and was, of course, the location of the warehouse in which Barnes had been found by PC Dobbs. The third piece lay on Beckman Street, a short cul-de-sac running due west from near the south end of Montgomery Road, the long road which runs north from Commercial Road up towards Stepney. I remembered from our discussion the previous evening that Beckman Street was Barnes's home address. I was still contemplating these matchsticks on the map and wondering what was in Holmes's mind when my thoughts were interrupted by the arrival of the maid with my breakfast tray.

As I ate, I pondered the matter further, my thoughts so abstracted that I scarcely noticed what I was eating. Then, all at once, a fresh thought struck me. I put down my tea cup and crossed to the chemical bench once more. For a minute or two I studied again the streets which lay between Wapping, where Barnes had worked, and the southern part of Stepney, where he had lived. Yes, I was right: although there were a number of different routes Barnes could have taken on his way home from work, the shortest, most direct way would almost certainly have included Dartmouth Street, in which Bailey Brothers' warehouse stood. Thus, unless he had made a specific *detour* to call somewhere on his way home, he would probably have passed the warehouse every day of the week. But what, if anything, did this suggest?

As I considered the matter further in the light of this observation, I thought for a moment that it suggested that the warehouse in question would be one of the likeliest places for Barnes to burgle. Passing the warehouse every day, he would probably have gotten to know what was stored there and whether it was worth stealing or not. He would quite possibly, also, have become familiar with the regular routines at the warehouse – when the men who worked there locked up and went home for the day, whether a night-watchman was employed there and so on.

I had no sooner reached this conclusion, however, than I saw that one could just as well argue the exact opposite, that this particular warehouse was probably the very last place that Barnes would choose to burgle. For if he had passed it every day, it was quite likely that he had been seen to do so by others, including the local police-constable on his beat. Indeed, PC Dobbs, who had found Barnes, had mentioned that he had several times seen him in the street in the late evening. In that case, if the burglary had gone off as planned and Barnes had got away without mishap, he would almost certainly have been one of the first people the police would have questioned about the matter, not necessarily to accuse him of being involved in the crime, but simply to find out if he had observed anything suspicious as he passed by the warehouse. But such questioning by the police was, I imagined, one of the last things that petty criminals would welcome. For however much he might try to conceal it, a guilty man is always anxious lest he give himself away, and that anxiety can quickly be recognized by an experienced detective officer.

Having thus argued myself to a stalemate on the question, I could make no further progress, and remained unsure as to what had been in Holmes's mind when he placed his matchsticks on the map. On another aspect of the case, however, it did later occur to me that we had perhaps been a trifle too quick to dismiss from consideration some of the tenants of the office building at 141, Victoria Street. After all, although it was certainly unlikely that the house-agents, the importers of Russian *objets-d'art* and the rest of them had any connection with petty criminals in the East End, it was always possible that one of these respectable firms unknowingly employed some individual who did have such a connection. That aspect of the case was certainly a profound mystery, and I wondered if Holmes, or Lestrade himself, would discover anything which might cast light on the matter.

It was late in the afternoon when Sherlock Holmes returned. He greeted me cheerily enough as he rang for a pot of tea, but he appeared a little weary. He threw off his hat and coat, dropped into a chair and took up his old clay pipe. Then, for several minutes, we sat in silence as he filled his pipe, lit it and sat puffing away contentedly. At length I could contain my curiosity no longer.

"Have you had any success with the case?" I asked.

"Yes, I have had some success," replied my friend, although there was something in his tone which seemed to suggest that he was not entirely satisfied.

"But not complete success?" I queried.

"Well, well," said he after a moment. "Lestrade consulted me on the matter, I have given him my opinion, and it is now up to Lestrade himself to complete the practical details – if he can."

"I should be most interested to hear about it."

"And I to recount it, when – Ah! Here is the tea! Let us refresh ourselves, and then I shall give you a full account of the matter. There are one or two instructive points in it, which I think you will find of interest."

A few minutes later, suitably refreshed, he continued:

"Before I begin," said he, "I should like to know if the markers I left on the map suggested anything to you."

"Indeed," I replied and described to him my reflections on the matter and the unsatisfactory conclusions I had reached. "So you see," I said, "although it seems likely that Barnes might have passed Bailey Brothers' warehouse every day of the week, I could not see that that really proved anything, one way or the other, about the robbery itself."

"You are quite right," returned my friend. "It is always a mistake to try to read too much into simple facts, which can very often be interpreted in diametrically opposite directions. But you correctly perceived the meaning of the matchsticks, Watson, by which I simply wished to indicate that, as you say, Dartmouth Street was the natural way for Barnes to go to and from his work. Of course, this does not in itself 'prove' anything, but it allows for the possibility – which Lestrade did not seem to appreciate – that Barnes's presence there on the evening PC Dobbs found him might not have been at all indicative of criminal intent on his part: on the contrary, we have every right, logically speaking, to expect him to have been there, on that evening as on every other, and it is thus possible that he may have had no involvement with the robbery whatsoever."

"But he was found inside the warehouse."

"Yes, that is true. But he may have gone in there simply because he saw something as he passed which caught his attention and led him to think that something was amiss, in which case he would be a perfectly innocent party. So I reasoned, anyhow. I could not, of course, say for certain that that was so, but it was at least a possibility, and I therefore kept an open mind on the question.

"Bearing this in mind, I had decided before I set off this morning that I should like to know a little more about the character and habits of Alf Barnes, so I made Benson's timber-yard, where he had been employed, my first port of call. There I saw Mr. George Benson, one of the owners of the business, who acts as general manager. He told me that he had been very sorry to hear about Barnes's death, for he had liked the man, which, as he informed me, was not always the case with his employees.

"'Did you know when you took him on that he had served a spell in prison?' I asked.

"'Yes,' said he. 'He was quite open about that. But there was something I liked about him when I interviewed him for the job, so I thought I'd take a chance with him. I must say I never regretted doing so. Although he had little education, he was interesting to talk to, and got on well with everybody who worked here. His work was not particularly demanding, but he attended to it very diligently. The chief part of it was to keep the place neat and tidy, to clear up after the men who were cutting the wood and so on, which makes a lot of mess. For that reason, he generally started work later in the day than everybody else and stayed later after the others had gone home. After he had been here a few weeks and had got used to the work, the whole place began to look more spick and span than it ever had before, in all the time I had been here.'

"'He sounds a model employee,' I remarked.

"'He was,' said Benson in an emphatic tone. 'I only wish everyone else was as good. He was also very trustworthy. For the first year he was here, I was always here in the evening, too, working on the accounts, sorting the sales documents and that sort of thing, and Barnes left when I did. But a year ago I gave him his own key and told him to lock up when he left. I don't think I have ever seen anyone look so pleased about anything. I gave him a small increase in his wages at the same time, for which he thanked me, but I don't think he was half so pleased about that as he was about being trusted with the key.'

"'What were his usual hours of work?' I asked.

"'He generally worked in the evenings, from two in the afternoon until about ten at night.'

"You can imagine how interesting this information was to me, Watson. It meant that Barnes would have been making his way home every night between ten and half-past. Thus the assumption that PC Dobbs had made when he had seen Barnes at that time of day, that he was returning from an evening spent in an ale-house, was almost certainly mistaken. On the contrary, Barnes had simply been walking home from his employment. The picture of Barnes which Lestrade had painted for us, then, of a criminally inclined drunk, was thus quite expunged, and another picture, that of a sober, industrious and trusted worker took its place.

"After leaving Benson's wood-yard, I made my way to the police-station, where Barnes's body was lying. There I was able to confirm for myself the man's injuries as they had been described to us, but did not learn very much more. One thing I did observe, however, was that Barnes had been using some kind of hair-dye. This was a surprising and puzzling discovery. I might have dismissed it as a trivial matter, an excusable vanity, if his hair had been turning grey, but that did not appear to be the case. While I was at the police station, a message was received from Lestrade, saying that he had completed his enquiries in the West End and would be coming to join me later, so I left a message of my own, informing him that I had taken the key and was going to Barnes's house, in Beckman Street.

"Beckman Street is a short, drab little cul-de-sac, Watson, with a dingy-looking row of smoke-begrimed terraced houses on either side. The inside of number thirteen, where Barnes had lived, was as drab and plain as the exterior, but was at least neat and tidy. A few items of frayed and worn furniture were placed in an orderly way about the place, but there was nothing of any interest there. A couple of books and magazines lying on the kitchen table offered the only suggestion in the whole house of any recreation or pleasure in life."

"It does not sound a very cheering place to come home to," I remarked.

Holmes nodded. "That is certainly how it struck me," said he. "I think that Barnes's long period of incarceration in Wormwood Scrubs had perhaps driven much of the *joie-de-vivre* from his life. I wandered from room to room, upstairs and downstairs, seeing all that was to be seen, but there wasn't very much. Two things only are worthy of mention. In the kitchen, beside the sink, was a bottle of hair-dye and a little brush for applying it, which confirmed the observation I had made at the police station. I confess I stood and gazed at this for some time. There seemed something so very incongruous about it. Why would someone who appeared to take little pleasure in life have gone to the trouble of using hair-dye? I felt there must be some special significance in it, but I could not think what that significance might be.

"The second interesting thing was a picture – an old photograph – which was hanging on the parlour wall. I had glanced at it earlier, but now I returned to it and examined it more closely. It was a formally posed photograph of a middle-aged man and woman – presumably man and wife – sitting down, with a small child – a boy of about eight – standing in front of them. The clothes they were wearing appeared to be those of thirty or more years ago. The photograph was obviously of some significance to Alf Barnes, as it was the only such picture in the whole house, and as I studied it, I wondered if the adults might not perhaps be his mother and father, and the child Barnes himself.

"One feature of the picture which caught my eye was the woman's hair. It was arranged in a very formal way – no doubt she had had it specially dressed for the occasion – but at the front, a clump of the hair – what one might, I suppose, call a forelock – was a distinctly lighter shade than the rest. I was unsure at first whether this was a natural, if unusual feature, or was the result of art, but then I noticed that the little boy's hair displayed exactly the same feature. I had not observed this at first because the boy's hair was fairly short, and the photograph was not a very clear one. As I gazed at this, comparing in my mind the boy's hair and features with those of Alf Barnes, I became convinced of two things: first, that the two – the boy and Alf Barnes – were indeed one and the same person, and, second, that Barnes had used the hair-dye specifically to darken his lighter-coloured forelock. But what, I asked myself, could this mean?"

"It sounds from your description a very unusual feature which anyone would recognize," I remarked. "Perhaps Barnes was ashamed of his criminal past or of his time in prison, and did not wish to draw attention to himself."

Holmes nodded his head. "And yet," he said, "I couldn't believe the effect would be sufficient to achieve that end."

"What do you mean?" I asked.

"For those who did not know Barnes from before his time in prison, what he did with his hair would be immaterial. On the other hand, those who did know him would, I think, have recognized him whatever he did to his hair. And yet, as I considered the question, I was inclined to agree with your suggestion, Watson, and thought it must be something to do with his crime or his prison sentence. As it happens, one of the seven hypotheses I had devised to explain the whole business could readily accommodate this new feature, and I decided to waste no more time in putting that particular hypothesis to the test.

"I locked up Barnes's house and made my way to the corner of Beckman Street, where it joins Montgomery Road. Most of the streets in that district are quite short, but Montgomery Road is the exception, being very long. It runs roughly southwest to northeast, towards Stepney. I proceeded northwards up this long road, looking at the door-numbers as I passed them. I dare say you can perceive what I was looking for, and what I expected to find there."

"On the contrary," I replied, "I haven't the faintest idea."

Holmes chuckled at this honest expression of mystification. "No doubt you will see it in a moment, then," said he, "as my account progresses. After some time I reached the house I was seeking and knocked briskly on the door. It was opened a moment later by a little girl, about nine or ten years old. I am sure people would say she was a charming child, but I didn't really notice. What seized my whole attention was the forelock of her hair, which was several shades lighter than the rest of it. Here, in an instant, was a ringing confirmation of my hypothesis."

"Barnes's child!" I cried in surprise.

"So I surmised," said Holmes. "'Is your mother in?' I asked her. She turned from the door, vanished from my sight and I heard her calling her mother. After a few moments a woman appeared in the doorway, drying her hands on a small towel.

"'Yes, sir?' said she. 'What is it?'

"'I imagine you have heard about Alf Barnes,' I said.

"She nodded her head and made to speak, but her feelings overcame her and she bit her lip.

"'I regret the necessity of raising the matter with you,' I said as she dabbed her eyes with the towel, 'but I am trying to get to the bottom of the case, which has, I believe, been misunderstood.'

"'Are you from the police?' she asked.

"'No,' I replied, 'but they were puzzled about the matter and asked me to look into it for them. May I come in for a moment?'

"She nodded her head without speaking, and I followed her into the small parlour.

"'You are, I take it, Alf Barnes's wife?' I said as we sat down.

"'Yes, sir.'

"'But have been living under the name of Mrs. Street?'

"'Yes, sir. 'Street' was my maiden name. Alf told me to go back to it after he got locked up. He said he didn't want me to be associated with a convict.

"'Particularly for the sake of your daughter, I imagine.'

"'Yes, sir, exactly.'

"'Whose name is Victoria.'

"'That's right, sir. You seem to know all about us.'

"'Well, well. I have had to work it all out for myself. The police don't know about you or Victoria, and are on a wild-goose-chase for non-existent clues at the moment. They believe that Alf died while attempting to rob the warehouse, but I believe the opposite: that he died while trying to prevent a robbery.'

"'Can this really be true, sir?' she asked.

"'So I believe. But in order to prove his innocence, I need some more information. Do you know either Daniel Wolfe or Dick Cross?'

"At the mention of these names, Mrs. Street pulled a face. 'They're villains, both of them,' she said. 'Neither of them's ever done an honest day's work in their lives. It was them as got Alf into trouble in the first place. And when they'd got him into trouble, they left him there and lied about him. They both said he'd organized the robbery himself, which wasn't true, and said they'd had nothing to do with it – and that wasn't true, neither.'

"'Do you know where either of these men are living now?'

"'Not exactly. I see them about sometimes. I think Wolfe lives in Peterborough Street – that's the third turning on the left down the road – and Cross lives in Swansea Street – that's a bit further down on the other side.'

"'Does either of them own a horse and cart?'

"'Wolfe has a cart. I've seen him on it. I think he hires a horse from somebody when he needs it. He goes out collecting old rubbish, but I think that's just an excuse to look into people's backyards to see if there's anything there worth stealing.'

"'Did Alf see much of either of them after he was released from prison?' I asked.

"'No, he didn't. He avoided them. To be honest, he hated them for what they'd done to him and what they'd done to other people.'

"'Do you know if there is any other man associated with them?'

"'I don't think so,' she replied with a frown. 'Except,' she added, 'a young lad, David Webster, who I've seen about with them a few times. He's only about seventeen or eighteen. I remember Alf mentioning him to me one day and saying what a fool he was. 'Wolfe and Cross will only get him into trouble,' he said, 'and then abandon him, like they did with me.' Alf was really angry about it, I remember. I've hardly ever seen him so upset about anything.'

"I thanked her and made a note of this information, all of which strengthened my own hypothesis of what had happened on Monday evening. My view, you see, Watson, was that something quite out of the ordinary must have occurred to lead Barnes to enter that warehouse. If you will put yourself in Barnes's shoes for a moment, you will see what I mean. Here is a man with a criminal record, who has served time in prison. Should he see a crime in progress, his natural inclination will be to keep well clear of it and pretend he has seen nothing, for he will fear that should the authorities make any connection between him and the crime, however mistaken and unfair, they will not believe him, but will pursue him and hound him until he is back in prison again. And yet, despite this perfectly understandable inclination to prudence, Barnes, as I believe, saw something which caused him to enter the warehouse and thus put his own freedom in jeopardy. What could this have been? It must, I believe, have been something more compelling than simply a door that was ajar."

"What, then?"

"I believe he saw Cross and Wolfe with the young lad, Webster. We know from Mrs. Street's testimony how angry Barnes was at the way the older men were corrupting Webster and leading him astray; perhaps he entered the warehouse to give them a piece of his mind on the subject, and to try to get Webster to leave."

"From what we have heard, that certainly sounds possible," I agreed. "And then, no doubt, in the ensuing quarrel, one of them – Cross or Wolfe – pushed him off the walkway."

Holmes nodded. "That is what I believe happened," said he. "Having reached this conclusion, I made to leave, but Mrs. Street was keen to talk, so I stayed a little longer. 'It must have been difficult for you when Alf was locked up,' I said to her.

"She nodded. 'It weren't easy. But I do washing and ironing for other folk, and just about scrape by.'

"'Have you seen much of Alf since he got out?'

"'Every week, on his day off, he'd come round here, regular as clockwork. We used to chat, and he'd often slip me a bit of money if he could afford it. I told him he was welcome to move back in here any time, and it would be cheaper for all of us if he did, but he wouldn't hear of it. He loved to see Vicky, but he was terrified she would find out that he was her father and he'd been in prison.'

"'I understand. You probably haven't heard, but Alf had some money with him when he died, in a pouch he kept with him all the time. I believe, from what he said just before he died, that he wanted your daughter to have it.'

"'That'd be just like Alf,' said she, biting her lip and dabbing her eyes again.

"'At the moment, though,' I said, 'the police are looking after the money, and we can't do anything about it. But I should think that when I've got the whole matter sorted out we'll be able to convince the authorities that you and Victoria are the rightful recipients of it.'

"'Thank you, sir,' said she.

"'Don't mention it,' said I. 'It is I who should thank you. Your information has been very helpful to me. I'm going back to the police station now, and, with a little luck, should be able to get the police off the wrong track and onto the right track before the day is out.'

"I left her then, Watson, and made my way through the drab, foggy streets to the police station, considering that my day so far had been well spent. I had made several bold conjectures, and all of them had proved correct. As I mentioned before, my opinion was that Barnes's use of hair-dye would not have been sufficient to prevent those who knew him from recognizing him. It might be, however, I conjectured, for a child who was too young to remember him from before his time in prison. But I doubted that he would have been too concerned about what a child thought of him unless that child were his own. If that were the case, the child might well have the same unusual hair as he had, and if Barnes wished to conceal the relationship between the two of them, his use of the hair-dye to alter the appearance of his own hair would be perfectly explained. Furthermore, if this child I had hypothesised really did exist, then it would surely be the most natural recipient for the money Barnes had asked PC Dobbs to take. Perhaps, then, I conjectured further, his repeated references to 'Victoria Street' were not to the thoroughfare in the West End, nor any other thoroughfare, but to a person, namely the child herself, a daughter by the name of Victoria. This was certainly possible, I judged, for 'Street' is a not uncommon surname.

"But what, then, I wondered could be the meaning of the 'one hundred and forty-one' which he also repeated several times? Most likely, I thought, it was indeed a house-number, in some other street which Barnes had failed to specify, either because in his distraction he forgot or because it seemed to him too obvious to need mentioning. Now, his daughter must live in the same district as Barnes himself, I reasoned – there would be no point in his attempting to disguise his hair otherwise – and the only residential street in those parts long enough to contain a house-number as large as 141 is Montgomery Road. That, then, was the house I was seeking when I left Beckman Street and set off up that long road. Now, encouraged by my success in finding the correct 'Victoria Street', and by the information her mother had given me, I was confident that my theory as to what had occurred on Monday evening was the correct one, that Barnes had been innocently walking home from work at his usual time and by his usual route when he had chanced to see something which had caused him to believe that Wolfe, Cross and the young lad, Webster, were engaged in robbing the warehouse. This, I believe, was the reason he entered the warehouse, where he probably quarrelled with them over their corruption of young Webster, and ended up by being pushed from the walkway to his death, as you suggested, Watson. The other three had then, I conjectured, made their escape on their builder's cart, with the stolen furs stuffed into those empty sand and cement sacks which PC Dobbs saw but did not examine. As far as I could see, this theory was the only one which not only solved the crime, but explained all the puzzling details.

"When I reached the police station, I found that Inspector Lestrade was already there, in confabulation with

Inspector Stanley. Lestrade informed me that he had ascertained that none of the tenants of 141 Victoria Street in Westminster had ever had occasion to use Bailey Brother's warehouse in Dartmouth Street, nor any other in that vicinity. This, as you will appreciate, came as little surprise to me, but I waited patiently until he had finished his account, before beginning my own. At first, he and Inspector Stanley were disinclined to believe my theory, chiefly, so it seemed to me, because they had not thought of it themselves, but as I explained my reasoning – the details of which I have described to you – they were at length forced to agree that my account of the matter was almost certainly the correct one.

"Having reached agreement, we then discussed what was to be done. I argued that they should waste no time in getting search warrants for the premises occupied by the three men I believed had been involved in the robbery. My view was that they would have heard that Barnes had died and, realising that any arrest might therefore involve a capital charge, would probably have been too afraid to try to dispose of the stolen furs, and would very likely, therefore, still have them. And that, Watson, is that. Whether Lestrade and Stanley have yet been able to organize a search party, and, if so, whether they have met with any success, I have no idea."

It was after eight o'clock that evening when there came a ring at our doorbell. A moment later, Inspector Lestrade bustled into our sitting room.

"You look pleased with yourself, Lestrade," remarked Holmes with a chuckle.

"So I should be," returned the policeman with a broad smile, seating himself on the chair I had pulled up for him in front of the fire. "I thought that as you had taken part in our discussion earlier, Mr. Holmes, I would let you know how we got on. You recall the plan Inspector Stanley and I decided upon, to make a thorough search of the houses of those villains, Wolfe, Cross and Webster?"

"Indeed I do," replied Holmes with another chuckle.

"We managed to get the necessary warrants a couple of hours after you had gone, and set off with four of the biggest constables in the division, just in case there should be any trouble. Our search didn't get off to a very good start, though: We turned Cross's house and outbuildings upside-down without finding anything, and then had no more luck at Wolfe's place. We didn't have young Webster's address, so I asked Wolfe what it was.

"'Who?' says he. 'Webster? Never heard of him.'

"'Yes, you have, Dan,' said his wife, who was there and who, I could see, just wanted to be rid of us as quickly as possible. She started to tell us the address, and her husband started shouting at her and then launched as vicious an attack on her as I have ever seen. I had to use the truncheon on him to quiet him down, and I can't say it troubled me to do so. Besides, it gave me an excuse to arrest him there and then and not wait any longer. He's a nasty piece of work, Mr. Holmes, and it will be good for everybody if he's taken out of circulation for a while.

"We made our way to the address we'd been given. Of course, Webster denied knowing anything about the business, just as the other two had done, but it didn't take us long to find the evidence that proved him a liar. In a coal-shed, in the yard behind the house, we found half a dozen cement sacks stuffed full of the stolen furs, which proved, of course, that our theory was exactly right in every detail."

"Congratulations!" cried Holmes. "It sounds as if you have brought the case to a successful conclusion!"

"I certainly have," returned the policeman, whose chest seemed to swell with pride at Holmes's praise. "All these villains are now safely locked up at the station. They are being questioned separately, and I don't think it will be long before they're singing like canaries, each of them blaming the others in order to save his own skin. There is no honour among thieves, you know!"

When Lestrade had left us, I turned to my friend. "Why," I cried indignantly, "the cheek of the man! He refers to 'their' plan and 'their' theory, when it was you who had suggested it all to them in the first place! I am surprised you did not say something to correct him!"

Holmes threw his head back and roared with laughter for several minutes, until he was almost limp with the effort. "My dear fellow!" said he at last. "You have been good enough to take an interest in my work in the last year or two. You should therefore have learnt by now that there is no necessary connection between he who does all the work and he who receives all the praise. It is for this reason that in such cases – and there are many of them – the work itself must be its own reward, and I must be satisfied with that!"

Lestrade's prediction, that the villains would inform against each other in an attempt to avoid conviction, proved accurate. In particular, the young lad, encouraged to do so by his family, turned Queen's evidence against the two men who had sought to take advantage of his youthful gullibility and inexperience. As a result, both Wolfe and Cross received lengthy prison sentences. On the capital charge concerning the death of Alf Barnes, they were acquitted, the jury finding the evidence insufficient to prove that either of them had had the intention of causing his death. Barnes himself was completely exonerated of any involvement in the crime, and, in due course, the money he had been saving for his wife and daughter was handed over to them, as we learnt from a touching letter which was received at Baker Street some months later from Barnes's widow, Mrs. Street.

THE INN ON THE MARSH

IN GLANCING OVER THE RECORDS I kept during the time I shared chambers with my eminent friend, the renowned detective, Mr. Sherlock Holmes, I am struck by the many occasions on which what appeared at the outset to be but a trivial affair became, in the end, a deadly serious investigation. Not infrequently, too, a case which began in London would oblige us to travel far beyond the capital and deep into the countryside in search of a solution. The case associated with The Wild Goose of Welborne, which I shall now recount, provides a good illustration of both of these points.

It was a pleasant, breezy day during the first week of September, 1883, the sort of weather that seems to freshen the air after the heat of the summer, and freshen, too, one's own energies and aspirations. Holmes and I had both spent the morning endeavouring to tidy and bring order to the sheaves of papers and documents which had built up on every surface during the previous months. We were about to take lunch, satisfied with our morning's work, when a ring at the doorbell announced a visitor. A moment later, our landlady ushered a young couple into our sitting-room, announced as Mr. and Mrs. Philip Whittle.

"I am sorry to intrude if you are eating," the young man said in an apologetic tone, "but this was the only time I could get away from work to see you."

"Not at all," returned Holmes affably, putting down his knife and fork and standing up from the table. "One can eat at any time. I had much rather hear what it is that has brought you here to see us."

"We have had a very odd experience," said the young man, as he and his wife seated themselves on the chairs I brought forward. "We cannot think what to make of it."

"The details, if you please," said Holmes.

"It is soon enough told. We stayed recently for a few days at an old inn, The Wild Goose, which lies in the marshland near the north Norfolk coast. It is the second time we have stayed there. The first time was at the beginning of June, when we stayed there for a week."

"Upon the occasion of your honeymoon, no doubt."

The young man looked surprised. "Yes, it was, as a matter of fact," said he, "but how did *you* know?"

Sherlock Holmes chuckled in that odd, noiseless fashion which was peculiar to him. "Since your wife removed her gloves, she has been displaying two very fine rings upon the third finger of her left hand. One is undoubtedly a wedding ring, and the other, with a sparkling stone in it, is no doubt an engagement ring. They both appear relatively new and shiny, and, moreover, the wedding ring is still a little loose, as is apparent when your wife touches it with the fingers of her other hand, which she has done several times already. It demands no great leap of logic to surmise that your wedding took place not very long ago, and that your week's holiday in Norfolk constituted your honeymoon."

The young lady flushed to the roots of her hair.

"I apologize for alluding to your personal circumstances," said Holmes quickly in an urbane tone. "It is a little hobby of mine – trifling and no doubt silly – to deduce facts about people from their personal appearance."

"That is perfectly all right," said Mrs. Whittle with a little smile.

"Such a hobby may prove useful in this case, if it helps you get to the bottom of the matter," remarked Whittle. "We were married at the very end of May, and immediately took a week's holiday in Norfolk, as you surmised. One or two of my married friends had spent their honeymoons at the seaside, at Margate, Brighton and places like that, but my fancy was for somewhere a little quieter, and Prudence agreed. When we heard from a cousin of mine of The Wild Goose, on the Welborne Marsh in Norfolk, it sounded ideal. It is a wild and beautiful spot, very popular with bird-watchers, I understand, as it is a haven for birds of all kinds. We spent most of the week there, in walks over the countryside or by the sea, and when we moved to Cromer, for the last two days of our holiday – even though Cromer itself is a quiet, charming and select sort of seaside town – it seemed to us very noisy and bustling compared with where we had been staying.

"We had enjoyed our stay at The Wild Goose so much that when the opportunity arose recently to take another brief holiday, both Prudence and I at once thought of returning there. We therefore travelled down to Norfolk last Friday, and stayed until Monday morning. However, the pleasure of being there, which we had been looking forward to so much, was marred by one odd little circumstance. As I was entering our details in the register, I turned the pages back to see the entries for the beginning of June, with Prudence looking over my shoulder. You will appreciate, no doubt, that the occasion of our honeymoon meant a lot to us both, and the urge to see 'Mr. and Mrs. Whittle' written somewhere for the first time was irresistible. Imagine our astonishment and dismay, then, to see that on the week in question there was no trace of our names whatsoever! Of course, I looked on the page before and the page after, but we were not there. Our names had simply vanished from the book completely, as if our visit to The Wild Goose had never taken place!"

Holmes rubbed his hands together in delight, a look of interest on his face.

"Did it appear to you that a page had been removed from the book?" he asked.

Whittle shook his head. "Perhaps it had, but if so, it must have been done very neatly, for I didn't notice anything of the sort. Besides, there were other names written in on the dates we had stayed there. It was not that everyone's name had disappeared from that week, just ours."

"Did you recognize any of these other names?"

"No, but I scarcely knew the name of anyone else that was staying there. We rather kept ourselves to ourselves, if you know what I mean, when we were there in June. As a matter of fact, it was very quiet then, anyway; there were very few other people staying there. I understand it gets much busier during the wild-fowling season. But the register now shows that a Miss Stebbing, a Mr. and Mrs. Williams and a Mr. and Mrs. Myers were staying there at the same time as we were, and I don't remember any of those people."

"Did you mention the matter to anyone at the inn?"

"I certainly did. I mentioned it to the girl who was attending us as we signed in. But she said she had only worked there for a month and didn't know anything about it. 'If you've got any questions,' she said, 'you'll have to ask Mr. Trunch.'"

"He being the landlord?"

"Exactly. I raised the matter with him that evening. He said he couldn't remember as far back as June. 'I have lots of visitors coming and going all the time,' he said. 'You can't expect me to remember everyone.' I pointed out to him that his memory was not the issue. Rather, it was the disappearance of our names from his register. He then suggested that we must be mistaken. 'I don't think you were ever here at all,' he said, and suggested that we had, rather, stayed at The Old Duck, which lies about three miles distant, across the marsh. Of course, it is ridiculous to suppose that a man could forget in three months where he had spent the very first holiday with his wife, but when I pointed that out to him, he became very irritable and almost abusive, and I had to let the matter drop. I must say his manner quite spoiled our memory of our previous visit there."

"It is certainly an odd experience," remarked Sherlock Holmes after a moment, "but there may be some rational explanation for it. Perhaps, for instance, a jug of water was accidentally spilled onto the register, rendering some of the pages illegible, including the one on which your names were written. Then, perhaps in attempting to rewrite the page from memory, someone has simply failed to recall your name. It may be that the 'Mr. and Mrs. Williams' which is now written in the book was someone's attempt to remember your name. Of course, that would not explain the landlord's unpleasant manner towards you. One would imagine that if such an explanation were the case, he would simply have informed you of the fact. But perhaps he has an unusually poor memory, and is embarrassed about it. Perhaps he drinks heavily. If so, he wouldn't be the first landlord of a remote country pub to consume all the profits in liquid measures, and I understand that excessive drinking has a very detrimental effect on the memory. Or is there something else?" he enquired, eyeing the young man closely.

Whittle nodded. "There has been a further development, which we have both found very upsetting, and for which such simple explanations cannot account."

"Very well. Pray proceed."

"We returned to London on Monday, having enjoyed our few days away despite the inauspicious beginning. Yesterday morning, however, this letter arrived by the first post." As he spoke, the young man took an envelope from his inside pocket and passed it to Holmes, who took from it a single sheet of paper which he unfolded upon his knee and studied intently for a few moments.

"What do you make of it, Watson?" said he, as he passed the letter to me and turned his attention to the envelope. The note, which was not signed, was a brief one, written in black ink in the centre of an oddly square-shaped sheet of paper, and ran as follows:

Asking many questions can be a dangerous course. Keep out of matters that do not concern you, and mind your business. This is a warning to you.

"What a very unpleasant and menacing letter!" I remarked to Whittle. "I am not surprised it has upset you both."

"It was posted in central London," said Holmes, "so it is unlikely to have come directly from the landlord of The Wild Goose himself. But the information that you have been 'asking questions' must surely have come from him, so he is evidently in communication with someone in London. The paper is unusually thick and heavy, and is an odd size. I wonder–"

He took his lens from the shelf and examined the letter closely through it. "Something has been cut off the top of the sheet," he said, "probably a printed heading which included an address. It has been carelessly done, though: there are a couple of tiny black marks at the top edge, where the scissors have clipped the bottom of a row of printed letters. There seems something familiar about it. Let me see–"

He sprang from his chair and began rummaging through the piles of old letters on his desk, which he had spent the morning putting in order. Presently he selected one and held it up beside the letter Whittle had received. "This is a letter of thanks I received from a client to whom I had been of service a few months ago," he said. "I think it is the same. Yes, undoubtedly it is the same. See," he continued, passing the sheets to our visitors. "The type of paper is a precise match, and the little traces of a line of printing that the scissors have left correspond exactly to this line on the other sheet."

"But that letter is from the German embassy!" I cried in astonishment, as I leaned over to verify his observations. "I cannot believe the German embassy would send such a crude threatening letter to Mr. and Mrs. Whittle! And why should they, anyway?"

Holmes nodded. "The Germans may be a forceful people, but – in my experience, at least – they like things to be done in a legal and proper manner. There is evidently nothing official about this letter. I imagine that someone employed at the embassy, acting on his own initiative, and without official sanction, has simply used a sheet of official notepaper as it was to hand, having cut the top couple of inches off to preserve, as he hoped, his anonymity."

"Then it is of no help to us in solving the problem."

"I should not say that, Watson. It confirms, after all, our suspicions that the writer of the note is probably a foreigner, as suggested by his incorrect rendering of the common idiom, 'mind your own business.' Can you recall, Mr. Whittle, if there were any foreigners staying at The Wild Goose at the time of your first visit there?"

"Yes," replied Whittle. "Now you mention it, I do recollect that there were two men there who I thought were probably foreign. One was middle-aged, with close-cropped sandy hair and a very large moustache, the other was a young fellow, about my own age, a little on the plump side. They kept very much to themselves and never spoke to us, but I overheard them talking once or twice. Sometimes they spoke in English, but with very strong accents, and sometimes in a foreign language. It may have been German for all I know – I am not familiar with that language, so I can't say."

"We thought they were probably keen bird-watchers," added Mrs. Whittle. "The landlord had told us that people come from all over Europe to study the birds on the Welborne Marsh."

"One evening when we were eating," Whittle continued, "a third man arrived and joined them at their table, a tall man with a bald head, and they all talked together very quietly. Later that evening, when we were in bed, I heard what sounded like a quarrel developing downstairs – raised voices and so on – and I remember wondering if it were those foreigners, but I fell asleep and heard no more."

"Nor me," added Mrs. Whittle. "Later in the night, though, I was abruptly awakened by a strange loud cry, as of pain or fear, and thought at first that it had come from downstairs. But when I mentioned it to the landlord in the morning, he said it was probably an owl, or one of the marshland birds, some of which have very strange cries that can sound almost human, he said."

"Anyway," continued Whittle, "the two foreign gentlemen left the next day, soon after breakfast. We didn't see the third man at all, so we presumed he'd left earlier, before we got up."

Holmes nodded his head and sat in silent thought for some time.

"I shall look into the matter for you," said he at length, addressing his visitors, "and let you know what I discover. As for the unpleasant letter you have received, I should not worry too much about it. It is a warning, after all, and not a direct threat, probably designed simply to deter you from asking any further questions. If you go about your daily business in your usual way, I don't think you will be troubled. However, it cannot hurt to observe due caution. Keep your eyes and ears open at all times, and avoid lonely places and dark alleyways."

When Mr. and Mrs. Whittle had left, Holmes hurried through his lunch and went out immediately afterwards. He returned two hours later, but there was a look of disappointment on his features.

"I have been scouring the back issues of the daily papers," he explained to me as he threw himself into an armchair by the hearth and took his old clay pipe from the rack. "My reasoning was that as the menacing letter had been posted in London and written on a sheet of paper from the German embassy, then the mystery was as much connected with London as it was with Norfolk, and the solution might as well be found here as there. However, all my efforts have uncovered precisely nothing, which is a somewhat frustrating result, although not so uncommon as you may suppose when you are compiling those records you keep of my successes."

"I don't imagine it helped that you didn't really know what you were looking for."

"A perceptive remark," said my friend, nodding his head. "I have looked closely at all the newspapers that appeared in the last week of May and the first week of June without finding anything there which refers in any relevant way to the German Empire, the Norfolk coast, German visitors to this country – whether to Norfolk or elsewhere – or anything else which might possibly have a bearing on the problem. However, I have learned one thing this afternoon."

"What is that?"

"That the Whittles were followed here earlier."

"How do you know?"

"Because I myself am now being followed. I observed the same man in three different places. I have no idea who he is, but he was clearly watching my every move."

"What will you do?"

"I think I shall run down to Norfolk and look into matters there. There are local papers there which may contain reports which did not reach the London Press. Perhaps I shall find some suggestive fact there. Unfortunately," he continued, with a glance at the clock, "although I could get down to Norwich this evening, it would be too late to do anything by the time I got there. I am thus obliged to sit here doing nothing until tomorrow, and I hate wasting time in this way."

I laughed, and my friend turned to me with a raised eyebrow. "I know what you are thinking, Watson," said he, "that you have never known a man to waste time in as thorough-going a fashion as I do on occasion. It is true. I do not deny it. If a national championship in time-wasting were to be held, I should probably set a new all-comers record. But that is when I have no case to engage my brain. When I am on a case, it is a different matter, and it is infuriating not to be able to get on as quickly as I would wish."

"You could go down to Norwich this evening, anyway," I suggested after a moment. "You could lodge for the night somewhere in the city centre, and make an early start in the morning."

"Of course, you are quite right, old man. That is the sensible course of action. It is only tiredness and irritation that prevented my seeing it. I will take your advice, Watson, on one condition."

"What is that?"

"That you accompany me."

"I should be delighted to do so. I was thinking only the other day that it would be pleasant to get away from London for a day or two before the nights start closing in."

"Then it is settled," said he, putting his pipe down and springing from his chair with a renewed vigour, "although I can't promise that you will find our expedition the holiday you have been looking forward to, Watson." He pulled open the top drawer of his desk, and, taking out his revolver, began to examine the chambers, then he glanced my way. "Pack a bag, then, old fellow, and let us be off!"

We caught the early evening train, reached Norwich just before nine o'clock, and put up at a small hotel near the station. In the morning we rose early, took breakfast at the hotel, and were in the office of the local newspaper, the Eastern Daily Press, soon after it opened. There we learned that as well as the daily newspaper, several weekly papers were also published, containing news specific to particular parts of the county. Holmes selected the daily papers of late May and early June, while I looked through the weeklies. Most of the news was trivial, or of purely local interest, and I was beginning to doubt we should find anything even remotely relevant, when my companion abruptly stopped his rapid page-turning.

"Hello!" said he. "Here is something, Watson!"

I leaned over to see what had caught his eye, and read the following:

CROWN PRINCE VISITS SHOE FACTORY

Prince Otto von Stamm, crown prince of Waldenstein, has this week visited a shoe factory in Norwich, where he was conducted round the premises in the company of the Lord Mayor, and was said to be greatly impressed by the modernity and efficiency he saw displayed there. Waldenstein has long been a notable producer of hides, but most are simply exported, and Prince Otto is keen to establish a leather-working industry within the principality to help alleviate the problem of unemployment.

"That sounds harmless and banal enough," I remarked.

"Yes, Watson, but it gives us, if not a German, then a German-speaker at least, in the county of Norfolk at the relevant time. Do you know anything of Prince Otto von Stamm?"

"He appears in the Society pages of the Morning Post fairly regularly," I replied. "I have frequently read such references as 'Prince Otto seems to prefer London to his homeland,' and 'We hear that Prince Otto has got himself into trouble again.' It is the usual sort of thing: a young foreign nobleman with more in his pockets than in his head. For some reason, London seems to act like a magnet to such people. I think he leads a fairly harum-scarum existence: visiting a shoe factory is the first sensible thing I've ever heard that he's done."

"Anything else?"

"Not really. I know he's fairly young – perhaps eight-and-twenty – but I know nothing else about him – and I know nothing whatever about Waldenstein, wherever that is."

"Waldenstein is one of those curiosities of European history," said Holmes. "It is one of the very few central European principalities which has not been swept up into the German Empire. It is very small – the population is probably not much greater than that of the town we are now in – and of no significance in itself. But its geographical position is a strategic one, lying adjacent as it does to both Germany and Austria. Its very existence creates a rivalry between the two great powers, both of which attempt to exercise an influence over it, and both of which would probably like to subsume it into their respective empires. Let us see if we can find anything else in these papers about Prince Otto's visit to Norfolk."

Our search for further reports on the young nobleman proved fruitless, but just as we were about to put the papers back in order, something caught my eye in one of the weeklies from the second week of June.

"This is a remarkable coincidence," I said.

"More on Prince Otto?"

"No, but a fellow-countryman of his, surprisingly enough." I folded the page over and read aloud the following report:

FOREIGN VISITOR PRESUMED LOST AT SEA

Franz Krankl, a visitor to Norfolk from the principality of Waldenstein, is missing, feared drowned, after a boat in which he had rowed out to sea on an angling expedition was found washed up on a beach near Sheringham. The owner of the boat, innkeeper and part-time fisherman, Albert Trunch of Welborne, says he had warned Krankl of the dangerous currents off the north coast of Norfolk, but Krankl had insisted he was very experienced in small boats. Herr Krankl holds a senior position in the government of Waldenstein, but was apparently here alone on a private holiday, and had been out of touch with his relatives for some time. A statement issued by the coast guard makes the point that all visitors must be made aware that there is a very great difference between conditions on inland waters and those encountered at sea.

"That is it!" cried Holmes. "It must be! Whittle informed us that the landlord of The Wild Goose was called Trunch, and now here is Trunch again, connected to a mysterious disappearance."

"It is certainly a striking coincidence."

Holmes shook his head. "It cannot simply be coincidence, Watson. The odds against it are enormous. Rather, these separate events are all links in a long chain of cause and effect, which will lead us to the truth. Trunch is clearly a link, so is this man Krankl, and so, I believe, is Prince Otto von Stamm, for I feel certain that he was the younger of the two men that the Whittles saw at the inn. It is to conceal his presence there, I believe, that the register has been altered."

"But if you are right," I said as we left the newspaper offices, "and it is Prince Otto's presence at The Wild Goose that someone is trying to conceal, why should the warning note to the Whittles have come from the German embassy?"

"As I understand it," Holmes replied, "Waldenstein does not have its own diplomatic representation in London. I believe that the German embassy acts on Waldenstein's behalf when necessary, in an informal sort of way. But someone at the German embassy may also, of course, have his own reasons for keeping the truth concealed. Don't look now, old fellow, but I think we are being followed."

"Is it the same man you saw in London?"

"I believe so. Anyhow, I observed this one – a man with a large moustache – outside our hotel this morning, and now he is outside the newspaper office. Evidently he – or a confederate – followed us to the railway station in London yesterday evening."

"What shall we do?"

"Nothing – or, at least, nothing other than what we were going to do anyway, which is to catch a train to Cromer, and make our way along the coast to the Welborne Marsh. It will be interesting to see if he comes with us."

The short branch train was already standing at the platform when we entered the station. We took seats in the compartment nearest to the front of the train, and Holmes positioned himself by the window, so that he could see anyone that came onto the platform. For almost ten minutes, he had nothing to report, then, just as the guard walked past our carriage after a consultation with the engine driver, and it was evident he was returning to his position at the rear of the train to give the signal to start, Holmes gave the "view-halloa."

"There he is!" cried he. "He has just broken cover, run onto the platform carrying a large leather bag, and climbed into the last compartment! He is following us to the coast!"

We reached Cromer in a little over fifty minutes, and hurried from the train to make sure we secured the station fly. Of the man apparently following us, there was no sign.

"He is lying low in his compartment," said Holmes under his breath, as we rattled off along the road by the station. "I saw the crown of his hat through the window. He evidently has no idea we have seen him."

Our journey took us at first through undulating countryside, but presently descended to low-lying, marshy terrain, where the narrow road meandered like a snake past rivulets and creeks, never far from the mud-flats and the sea. From time to time we heard the sound of distant gunshots, and saw the little puffs of smoke rising up from the hollows where the wild-fowlers crouched, waiting for the birds to fly their way. At length, after about half an hour, we reached a small, isolated village, which I saw from a sign was Welborne. The wind was blowing sharply off the sea now, the clouds overhead were dark grey, and there were a few spots of rain in the air. Our driver did not pause, but passed right through the village and on towards the sea. Half a mile farther on, we at last reached The Wild Goose. It was a low, spreading building, with grimy lime-washed walls and a weathered-looking thatched roof, and appeared as ancient as the ground upon which it stood.

"We don't yet have all the threads in our hands," said Holmes to me, when we had paid off our driver and stood before the weather-beaten front door of the inn, above which a painted sign depicting a flying goose swung and creaked in the wind. "We shall therefore have to approach the matter in an oblique way. If in doubt, just follow my lead."

He pushed open the door, and I followed him into the dark interior. After a moment, a young woman in an apron appeared through a doorway, but when Holmes asked if we might speak to the landlord, she informed us that he was out, and would not be back for another hour. We decided then to leave our bags at the inn and take a walk across the marsh towards the sea.

It was a wild, tempestuous day now, and the nearer we approached the sea, the stronger the wind became, and the more the gusts seemed to veer and shift about us. At length we surmounted a steep shingle bank, and there before us lay the broad, heaving expanse of ocean, the breakers pounding the shore with a boom and a crash, sending mountains of spray into the air which the sharp wind whipped into our faces. I opened my mouth to speak, but abandoned the attempt almost at once: the thunderous noise of the sea blotted out all other sounds. After we had stood shivering for a few minutes by this deafening maelstrom, Holmes plucked my sleeve and indicated that we should retire behind the shelter of the shingle bank.

"The sea is very rough today," said he as we crouched down in the lee of the bank. "I suppose you were reflecting on the conditions the unfortunate Herr Krankl may have encountered."

"Among other things, yes."

"I should not trouble yourself with that thought, Watson. As I read the matter, Krankl was never in a boat at all. I strongly suspect he lost his life at The Wild Goose, on the evening the Whittles heard a quarrel there."

"You believe he was the third man, the tall man who arrived one evening, but was nowhere to be seen the following morning?"

"That does seem to me the likeliest explanation. But, come, let us get back to the inn, and see if Trunch has returned yet."

At The Wild Goose, in answer to our query, Trunch himself appeared after a moment from some back room. He was an absolute giant of a man, a good six-foot-four if he was an inch, with a chest like an ox. For a moment he stood looking down upon us with an expression of disdain.

"Well?" said he at length.

"A friend of mine stayed here not long ago," Holmes began.

"What of it?"

"When he came again more recently, he found that his name had been removed from the register."

"Oh, *him!* A snivelling trouble-maker from London! If you're on the same errand, you can sling your hook!"

He made to turn away, but Holmes persisted:

"It is, of course, a criminal offence to fraudulently alter books used for accounting purposes. The authorities take a dim view of that sort of thing."

"Oh, *do* they? What is that to you, Mr. Know-all? Are you one of those blood-sucking tax-collectors yourself? No? Then listen, friend, and I'll tell you what my father told me when I was a young man. 'Mark my words, son,' he said to me: 'there's always some swine wanting money, and the best way of dealing with them is to tell them to go to Hell.'"

Sherlock Holmes remained unmoved. "Something else you may not be aware of is that to attempt to conceal something criminal is itself a crime. In attempting such concealment you also lay yourself open to being charged as an accessory to the original crime, even if you had nothing directly to do with it."

"Just what are you saying?" demanded Trunch. His voice was still loud and scornful, but there was a note in it now, too, of apprehension, and it was clear that Holmes's remarks had had an effect. Holmes himself evidently perceived this, for he quickly pressed home his advantage.

"We know that Prince Otto von Stamm was here, and the other men."

"What if they were?" said Trunch defiantly, but the tone of bluster in his voice was rapidly ebbing away, and it was clear he was on the defensive.

"Whatever occurred here, you, as landlord, will be held responsible–"

"What humbug!"

"–especially as you helped conceal the truth by fraudulently altering the register."

"Someone else pulled out the page. I had to re-write it from memory. There's no crime in that. What else could I do?"

"But you didn't put all the names in again, did you? You deliberately omitted some."

Trunch's bullying manner had quite disappeared now. It is difficult to say what might have happened next, but we were interrupted by the re-appearance of the young serving-woman. She whispered something to the landlord and he nodded his head. "Come this way," he said to us, "and I'll tell you what happened."

We followed him through the doorway, along a corridor and into a back room. As we entered, I saw a large leather bag lying open on a side-table. Holmes evidently saw it, too, for I saw him glance that way and stop. But it was too late, the door slammed shut behind us. We turned, to see a man with a large, straggling moustache, who had been concealed behind the open door. In his hands was a large double-barrelled shotgun, which he pointed at us.

"Leave them to me, Trunch," he said in a strong, guttural accent. "I'll deal with them." He yanked open a back door and indicated we should go out that way.

"Now," said he, when we were outside in a small backyard, the cold wind whistling about our ears, "start walking." All about us as we left the yard, the Welborne Marsh stretched away as far as the eye could see.

"Don't be a fool," said Holmes over his shoulder, as we followed a muddy, winding track. "If it's your intention to murder us here on the marsh, you'll never get away with it."

"You forget, Mr. Busybody, that the wild-fowling season has now begun," returned our captor from behind me. Even as he spoke there came the sound of gunshots – one, two, three – from all about us on the marsh. "Your deaths will be ascribed to an unfortunate sporting accident. Sadly, such things do happen."

"You murdering swine," I cried. "Don't think we don't know about Krankl! Soon everyone will know the truth!"

For an instant he was silent, but it was only for an instant. "So," he cried, in a voice full of venom. "If you're so interested in Krankl, I can show you where he is lying, and then you can join him there! Keep walking!" he snarled, thrusting the shotgun sharply into my back. My mind reeled. There must be something we could do – we could not simply walk quietly to our deaths – but panic had seized me, and I could think of nothing.

Ahead of me, Holmes walked on steadily, his shoulders hunched against the cold wind, his hands thrust into his coat pockets, as we made our way deeper into the wilderness of the marsh. "Slippery path, this one, Watson," said he over his shoulder. "Mind you don't lose your footing!"

For a brief moment, I confess I was surprised that, in our desperate situation, Holmes should make such a banal remark. Next moment, I realised that he was telling me he wished me to slip and fall to the ground, perhaps as a distraction. How that would help us, I could not imagine, but if that was what he wanted me to do, then that is what I would do.

A short distance further on, as the path breasted a small rise and dropped away into a shallow dip, I saw my opportunity. I deliberately let my left foot slide away in the mud, and, with a loud cry, tumbled to the ground. At once our captor lowered his shotgun and pointed it at me, but in the same instant there came the sharp crack of a pistol-shot. Holmes's hands were still in his pockets, and I realised he had turned and fired his revolver through the fabric of his overcoat. There came a cry of pain from our captor, as the shot caught him on the left arm, and he raised the shotgun towards Holmes. With every ounce of energy in my body, I sprang up and threw myself upon him, forcing the barrels of his gun upwards and to the side. The movement evidently jerked his finger against the triggers, and both barrels discharged with a deafening roar into the open sky above us, then, with a force I would not have believed myself capable of, I swung my fist up and struck him on the chin with the most perfect uppercut I have ever delivered, sending him sprawling backwards into the mud. I quickly picked up the gun which he had dropped as he fell, as Holmes covered him, his revolver held rock-steady in his hand.

"Good man," said my friend to me. "Your swift action saved us all. Are you all right?"

"I think I may have depressed the knuckle of my third finger," I remarked as I examined my right hand, wincing with pain as I touched the spot. "It will probably need setting. I am not much used to fisticuffs."

There came a cry from behind us. I turned, to see a young man hurrying towards us down the path from The Wild Goose. "Stop! Stop!" he cried, waving his arms in the air. As he came nearer I recognized him from pictures I had seen in the illustrated London papers as Prince Otto himself. "Stop at once!" he cried as he came up to us, breathing heavily, his cheeks flushed with effort. "I want no more violence on my account, Schnabel. I have decided to make a clean breast of everything. After all, it *was* an accident."

"Be quiet, you fool!" said the other man in a harsh tone, as he struggled unsteadily to his feet. "How did you get here?"

"I learned late last night in London where you had gone, and caught the first train I could this morning."

"Tell us about the accident you referred to," said Holmes, covering both of them with his pistol. "It is, I take it, to do with Krankl, and Waldenstein's foreign policy."

"Don't tell them anything," said Schnabel quickly, but Stamm ignored him.

"You appear well informed already," said he to us, "so you may be aware that my country has recently been in discussion with Austria, with a view to linking our future to theirs. This is the course long favoured by my father and his chief minister, Franz Krankl. However, Herr Schnabel here has been arguing on behalf of the German Empire that the better course is for us to favour his country. My father is frail and may not have much longer to live. When he dies and I succeed him, the decision will of course be mine, so it is something I must think about now.

"I was in this part of the country anyway, for some duty I had to perform, so Herr Schnabel and I arranged to meet for secret discussions at the most remote spot we could find, The Wild Goose. Unfortunately, Herr Krankl, who was also in England, got wind of what we had planned, and hurried here to try to dissuade me from this course of action. He arrived one evening and we quarrelled. I had had too much to drink, I admit, and was quite drunk. In the heat of the quarrel, I am ashamed to say, I lost my temper and struck out at him, he fell from his chair and hit his head so hard on the corner of the hearth that it killed him. Herr Schnabel here ushered me from the room – I was in no fit state to do anything sensible – and said he would deal with the matter. He disposed of the body somewhere on the marsh, and later bribed the inn-keeper, Trunch, to say that we had never been here, and that Krankl had hired his boat, put out to sea alone in it, and appeared to have been lost overboard."

"You have made a serious mistake," said Holmes.

"I know," returned Stamm. "I am ashamed of myself, both for being drunk, and for losing my temper with Krankl."

"That was not my meaning," said Holmes. "Your mistake was in permitting Schnabel to dispose of the body. Don't you see that that places you completely in his power?

At any time in the future he could, by threatening to expose the truth, blackmail you into doing precisely what he wished you to do."

"Don't listen to him, your Highness," cried Schnabel.

"I imagine that that has been his intention all along," continued Holmes, ignoring the other man's outburst, "to have this hold over you, so that he could force you to do his bidding, as a puppet-master controls his puppets. On the night Krankl was here, he saw his chance and seized it."

"It's a lie!" cried Schnabel.

"You don't even know for certain that Krankl was really dead when you left the room," Holmes persisted. "Perhaps he was only stunned, and was finished off later by Schnabel, after you had gone to bed. It would of course suit his purposes perfectly to be rid of Krankl, who was a staunch proponent of the Austrian alliance."

"That's lie number two!" interrupted Schnabel, his voice hoarse, but Holmes's words had evidently plucked a cord in the young nobleman's memory.

"I had wondered about that," he said, "wondered if I had really killed him or not. For even in my shamefully drunken state, I had noticed that Krankl's wound did not appear to be bleeding at all, and nor was there any sign of blood on the floor the following morning."

Abruptly, the infuriated Schnabel attempted to launch an attack on Holmes, but the latter levelled his pistol at him and he gave it up at once.

"The only way to decide the matter is to examine the body," said Holmes. "Schnabel says it is buried out this way on the marsh. Will you show us where it is?" he asked, turning to the German.

"No. You can find it yourself," Schnabel responded.

"Your lack of co-operation is disappointing," remarked Holmes. "I had only permitted you to drag us out here in the hope that you would lead us to where the unfortunate Herr Krankl lies buried. However, we shall find it soon enough. First, though, I think we'll all get back to the inn, and notify the authorities of what has occurred."

When we reached The Wild Goose, Trunch was nowhere to be seen, but his absence was soon explained, as the serving-girl informed us that he had gone to fetch the local constable, after declaring with great vehemence that he wished he had never become involved with these people. Just a few minutes later we heard a trap pull up outside the inn and Trunch entered, with a policeman who was almost as massive as Trunch himself. Holmes quickly explained to the policeman all that had taken place. This interview ended with Schnabel in handcuffs, and he and von Stamm going off with Trunch and the constable.

"I can't imagine what Mr. and Mrs. Whittle will think when they learn what you have discovered," I remarked to Holmes later that day, as we took lunch at a hotel in Cromer.

My friend chuckled. "Yes, it will certainly be strange for them to discover that as their honeymoon was taking its no doubt blissfully happy course, they were, all unaware, sharing a roof with international intrigue and murder!"

I heard later that the body of Franz Krankl had been recovered from a shallow grave on the marsh, but the medical examination and inquest which followed proved inconclusive. The cause of death was established with certainty as being the wound to the head, but the medical examiner stated that he could not be certain whether Krankl had been struck once, or more than once, and in the end a verdict of accidental death was recorded. Trunch, Schnabel and von Stamm were all convicted on their own admission of attempting to conceal the death, but taking various circumstances into account, and with no doubt half an eye on the diplomatic aspects of the case, the court took a lenient view and handed down relatively light sentences. Trunch therefore returned, no doubt a chastened man, to the inn on the marsh where he continued to cater for the needs of keen bird-watchers, and von Stamm and Schnabel returned to their homelands, and never, so far as I am aware, visited these shores again.

THE GREEN UMBRELLA

IN THE EARLY SPRING OF 1888, a remarkable series of bizarre and perplexing cases was laid before my friend, Mr. Sherlock Holmes, for solution. Among the headings in my notebooks for this period, I find recorded the singular problem of "The Oaken Door"; the baffling affair of "The Second Stair," a case in which several of the oldest families of the kingdom were involved so intimately; and the mysterious disappearance from the Scottish Express of the Barrington brothers and the Star of Golconda diamond, *en route* from London to Glasgow. Even in a period such as this, there were occasional days of frustrating inactivity, but for much of the time my friend was as busy as I had ever known him.

As might be expected, there were among these many cases a few which were not entirely successful from Holmes's point of view, but they nevertheless constitute an admirable wealth of material for his biographer, to the extent that it is only with the very greatest difficulty that I am able to select those which are to be included in these memoirs. In one respect, however, my task is simplified; for several of the more important cases have already received due prominence in the press, and little would be gained by my re-telling them. I am therefore inclined to draw for my present narrative upon that large number of cases which have previously been unreported, and which remain unknown beyond the circle in which the events took place. Among these latter cases is the story of the singular adventure which befell Mr. Horace Barclay, antiquary and collector of sporting prints, of Bedford.

Sherlock Holmes was fond of remarking on the unrivalled possibilities for mystery and confusion which the complex kaleidoscope of life in London offered so plentifully: the unimaginable crossing and re-crossing of separate threads of life which were inevitable in a city of four million souls, and which might lead, through the unseen workings of chance, to the most surprising and *outré* results. Few cases that I can recall have illustrated his thesis more vividly than the one which is forever associated in my mind with the green umbrella.

My notebook records that it was a cold and blustery day towards the end of March, in that period of the year when the harshness of winter begins at last to give way to the fresh delights of the spring, and even in the very heart of the brick fastness of London, the trees acknowledge the inevitability of the seasons, and show here and there the first green shoots upon their bare branches.

My friend had been without a case to engage his energies for a day or two, and already the idleness had begun to throw a visible strain upon his keen, active temperament. Several times that morning, as he had prowled about the rooms, for all the world like some caged, frustrated beast, I had watched with foreboding as his bright eyes had rested thoughtfully for a moment on the corner of the mantelpiece, where lay the small morocco case which contained his hypodermic syringe. Thus far, he had resisted the temptation, but I knew that even Holmes's iron will could not resist much longer the evil blandishments of the needle. After lunch, he had spent some time sifting through the stacks of old books which had accumulated in the corners of the room, tossing most of them aside with a groan, until he at length settled himself in a chair with a copy of Plutarch's *Moralia;* but he read little, and the expression of *ennui* never left his face. I had known him long enough to recognize the danger signals, and if he as a detective was in urgent need of a case upon which he could expend his energies, I as a medical man desired it no less on his behalf. Thus it was that when a sharp ring at the doorbell interrupted my thoughts, I listened with unusual attention to the sound of voices in the hall, and experienced an almost macabre sense of relief when, moments later, there came the step of an unfamiliar foot upon the stair.

A soberly dressed man was shown into the room. His dark frock-coat and top hat, and the solemn expression of his face, all indicated a man of conservative and serious-minded inclinations, and although he could scarcely have been more than two-and-thirty years of age, he had about him the grave air of one almost twice that age. The dark, expensive-looking valise which he carried in his hand served to confirm the general impression, but a singular and incongruous note was struck by his other item of luggage, a very large cotton umbrella, of a vivid emerald green, which he carried under his arm. He bowed slightly, and introduced himself as Horace Barclay.

"Pray, take a seat, Mr. Barclay," said my friend, putting down his book. "You appear a little fatigued by your railway-journey from Bedford."

Our visitor looked up sharply, as he lowered himself wearily into the armchair, and raised one eyebrow quizzically. "How do you know where I have travelled from?" he enquired, a tone of deep suspicion in his voice. "How came you by this information?"

"Tut, tut," said Holmes. "I have no information: I merely observe. When a man walks into my rooms with a slight but unmistakable trace of railway soot upon his hat, and a fresh copy of the *Bedford Gazette* rolled up in the handle of his travelling-bag, it is not so difficult to divine his origins."

A look of relief passed over our visitor's face, but there was still a frown of perplexity there, and he made no immediate response. After a moment, Holmes continued, in a thoughtful, pleasant voice:

"And yet," said he, "the journey from Bedford to London is not generally such a long one as to cause fatigue. Perhaps it is events since your arrival in London which have wearied you so. Yes? I thought as much, for I see that you have been in town for some time – perhaps an hour or two – and have had some walking to do – tut! there is no mystery; your shoes, my dear sir, tell their own story – which must have been tiring if you were obliged to carry that heavy bag with you the whole time, and on such a windy day as this! I think a strong cup of coffee would be of benefit to us all! If you would be so good as to ring for the maid, Watson!

"Now, Mr. Barclay," he continued: "You appear, if I may say so, a man of neat and methodical habits, yet you have come to consult me without having previously made an appointment – not at all, my dear sir! It occasions no difficulty: I mention the fact merely as a link in the chain of reasoning – and it therefore appears that your decision to consult me is a very recent one."

"Less than half an hour old," returned the other. "I was given your name and address by an official at King's Cross station – the only helpful person I have so far encountered since I arrived in London!"

"Quite. Let us see if we cannot swell the numbers of the helpful, then. If you would be so good as to explain in what way we may assist you? You hesitate. Perhaps I can help you? You have, I should say, the appearance of one on a pleasant trip up to town, intending to stay a night or two, perhaps with friends, perhaps at your club. No? With friends, then. But you bring with you a very large green umbrella, which appears more suited to outdoor pursuits." Our visitor's eyes rested momentarily on the umbrella with a look of distaste "Ah! I see! The umbrella is not yours. I suspected as much. You are bringing it for someone, then – for a friend – perhaps the friend you are coming to stay with? He left it at your house, perhaps, when last he was there? Yes? But you have not gone to his house, but have, rather, been tiring yourself, walking on London's crowded pavements. Why is that, I wonder? Perhaps you do not know his present address? Yes? You had arranged to meet, but you have somehow missed each other, and now you are at a loss as to what to do? In short, Mr. Barclay, you wish us to help you find your friend?

"You see, Watson," said Holmes with a chuckle, as our visitor nodded his head wearily, "we progress all the time! Soon we shall be able to dispense with interviews altogether. When clients call to consult us, we shall merely need to look them over to divine the problem, provide an answer and pocket the fee – nothing could be simpler! Thank you, Mary," he said gaily as the maid brought in the coffee. "If you would place the tray close to hand, I will do the rest.

"Now, Mr. Barclay," he continued, handing his visitor a cup. "I can let you have the names of three reliable private enquiry agents who specialize in matters of this sort. Fairclough is the best, but Parker and Richardson are also competent."

"I had hoped that you would undertake the job yourself, sir. I was told you are the best man in London."

"I am a consultant, sir: I do not usually undertake such simple tasks as this – and my fees reflect that fact."

"Nevertheless, Mr. Holmes, I should deem it a great favour. I do not feel I can drag myself, umbrella and bag round to any further addresses."

"Very well," said Sherlock Holmes, with a note of reluctance in his voice. He reached for his note-book from the side-table. "Pray, let us have the details, then: the name, if you please, of your friend – or acquaintance, perhaps, as you appear to be less than fully intimate with his movements, and do not know enough about him to trace his whereabouts for yourself."

"'Acquaintance' would indeed be more accurate, Mr. Holmes. His name is James Chambers, but there is little more that I can tell you about him. Therein lies the difficulty."

"We can at least make a start," returned Holmes. "Tell me," he said: "is Mr. Chambers a sportsman? When he stayed with you, was it for the fishing in the Ouse, perhaps? No? Nothing of the sort? Well, well, that is interesting. His umbrella is that of a sportsman, and hardly one for everyday use, and yet he did not engage in any activity which might have required it. We cannot trace him in that way, then."

Holmes tapped his pencil on his note-book in a thoughtful manner. "Perhaps," said he at length, "before you tell us all you can of Mr. Chambers, you could explain how you came to miss each other this morning. Was he not waiting for you at the meeting-place?"

"Of that I have no idea," replied our visitor. "I left King's Cross station rather hurriedly, and cannot say whether he was there or not."

"One moment," Holmes interrupted. "You say King's Cross station, but I take it you mean St. Pancras station."

"No; King's Cross."

"But surely the direct trains from Bedford arrive at St. Pancras?"

"Indeed they do, Mr. Holmes, but there were special circumstances which obliged me to travel by a different route today. Once at the station, I made a mistake, and left with the wrong person." His voice faltered as he spoke, and his face coloured bright red, to the roots of his hair.

"Oh?" said Holmes, a slight smile on his face.

"It is nothing," said the other in embarrassment. "It is quite irrelevant, and has no bearing on the matter. As a matter of fact, I left with a woman – a young lady, I mean – who, I believed, had come to meet me. I thought she must be Chambers's sister, and she seemed to mistake me for someone else, too. She was a very engaging, very pressing young woman. It was an unfortunate misunderstanding, but I suppose these things happen in London all the time. By the time we had realised our error and parted, Chambers was nowhere to be seen."

Without warning, Holmes burst out into a roar of laughter, and I must confess that I, too, found it difficult to suppress a chuckle.

"Pray forgive me, my dear sir," said he after a moment, almost choking in his mirth, "but your story is a singular one!"

His client's face assumed a look of annoyance.

"I am not used to being treated as a source of merriment," said he in a heated voice, and seemed about to stand up. But then the lines of his face softened, and he almost smiled. "I suppose it does sound a trifle absurd," said he after a moment, in a reflective tone. "Nothing like it has ever happened to me before. I am a bachelor, and live an extremely quiet and secluded life, as you will appreciate if I tell you a little about myself and how I came to meet James Chambers. My home, 'The Poplars,' lies on the outskirts of Bedford, where I devote much of my time to the study of prints and paintings of the last century, particularly those depicting sporting scenes, upon which I have written a couple of trifling monographs. My own collection of sporting prints is ranked among the best in the country, and although I deal, in a small way, in etchings, mezzotints and so on, it is scarcely a serious business, and chiefly consists of my selling on items which I have acquired at auction, and do not wish to keep for my own collection. I come to London only occasionally, generally in connection with this interest, but over the years I have made one or two friends here with whom it is my pleasure to dine from time to time. These friends are, in the main, those whose interests lie in the same fields as my own, and I might mention that they include Sir Basildon Wemyss and Lord Steeples among their number.

"It was at the house of Lord Steeples, a month or two ago, that I made the acquaintance of a young man by the name of Chambers. His manner was extremely pleasant, and when we discovered that our tastes in prints were very similar, we naturally fell into a deep and prolonged conversation on the matter. The upshot was that we attended an auction together, a few weeks later, during the course of which he asked if he might pay me a visit, and see for himself my collection, which he said he had heard described as 'the most complete panorama ever assembled of man and horse in the eighteenth century.' I was delighted to accede to his request, for I receive few visitors, and I invited him to stay for a couple of days. The thought of a fellow-collector to brighten my weekend was indeed a pleasant one. As a consequence of our discussion, he came to stay with me upon the following Friday, that is, two weeks ago, remaining at my house for three days.

"Shortly afterwards, I received a letter from him, addressed from the *Poste Restante* at Charing Cross post office, expressing his desire to return the compliment and put me up for a few days at his house in London. I wrote back agreeing to this proposal and suggesting a suitable date, whereupon I had a second letter from him, confirming the date and describing the arrangements which were to apply for my visit. He was in dispute with his landlord at the moment, so he informed me, over some unsatisfactory repairs which had been carried out to the roof of his house, and it had been suggested that the dispute might best be resolved by his moving to another of the landlord's properties. Because of this, he could not be certain of his address from one day to the next, which was why he was writing from a post office, but he assured me that the matter would be settled by the time of my visit, and suggested that he meet me at the railway station when I arrived in London. He added in a post-script that he believed that he had left an umbrella at my house, and asked me, if I found it, to bring it with me when I came."

"This is the umbrella in question, I take it," said Holmes, eyeing the gaudy object which lay upon our carpet. "It is certainly a bright object to overlook. One might have supposed that even if your friend forgot to take it with him when leaving, you would have noticed his omission."

"I did not know he had it with him. He must have had it inside his large bag when he arrived, and he never used it while there."

"Ah!" said Holmes, a note of interest in his voice. "Where did you find it?"

"It was pushed behind the wardrobe in the room Chambers had occupied when he stayed with me."

"Excellent!" said Holmes with a dry chuckle. "Pray continue with your most interesting narrative, Mr. Barclay!"

"In the week which followed, we exchanged a perfectly absurd series of letters. I wrote to advise him of the time my train would arrive at St. Pancras station, and added that I had indeed found his umbrella. He then replied that I should come to King's Cross station, which was far more convenient for him than St. Pancras. I wrote again immediately, explaining that to arrive at King's Cross at a reasonable hour I should have to start earlier, make a longer journey across country, and change trains at Sandy. I further pointed out to him that it was manifest nonsense to say that King's Cross was more convenient to him than St. Pancras, for the two stations stand side by side in the same street, and there can be no two railway termini in the world which are closer. Back came his reply by return of post. He acknowledged the sense of what I said, and apologized for having misled me, but added that he had feared to weary me with the true explanation of why he could not meet me at St. Pancras. He had once had a dispute with the Midland Railway Company, who had treated him, so he said, with the most odious discourtesy, as a result of which he had vowed never to use their trains nor enter their premises again. This struck me as a trifle absurd, especially as it was not he but I who would suffer by the arrangement, but, anxious only to draw the correspondence to a close, I wrote back finally, agreeing to his request."

Our visitor paused then and took a sip of coffee, and as he raised the cup to his lips, I observed that his hand trembled slightly.

"Today is the day I was to visit James Chambers," he continued after a moment, "but, as you can see, I have got no further than Baker Street, despite the fact that I arrived at King's Cross over two hours ago."

"The details of what has delayed you, if you please."

"It has absolutely nothing to do with my not being able to locate my friend."

"I think we should reserve our judgment on that question, Mr. Barclay. I find it a useful rule of thumb that when several surprising, but apparently separate incidents occur within a short space of time, there is often a connection between them. We have here, on the one hand, certain unusual features in the arrangements Mr. Chambers made with you, and his leaving his umbrella at your house in somewhat odd circumstances, and, on the other hand, your surprising encounter with a stranger at the railway station. I think we ought to hear the details of the latter before we attempt to reach any conclusions."

"Very well, I will tell you exactly what happened, although it is perfectly absurd. When the train pulled into the station, I alighted quickly, in an attempt to beat the crush at the ticket-barrier. Nevertheless, by the time I reached it, the platform seemed to be swarming with people, and it was some time before I could extricate myself from the throng. As I did so, and as I surveyed the vast sea of faces around me, which seemed to contain an example of every known species of humanity, a handsome and well-dressed young woman dashed suddenly through the crowd towards me, and, flinging her arms round my neck, gripped me in a passionate and unseemly embrace. Burdened as I was, with my heavy bag and this ridiculous umbrella, I was unable to fend off her advances, and, in any case, the speed at which she had executed her attack would in itself have been sufficient to preclude resistance.

"As I attempted to disentangle myself from her embrace, painfully conscious that I was the object of mirth in the crowd around, and convinced that the woman must be a monomaniac of some kind, and quite possibly dangerous, she suddenly spoke, in a gay but urgent voice, and I was surprised to hear that her accent and tone were of the most respectable and refined.

"'Come quickly,' said she. 'I have a cab waiting outside the side-entrance.' I evidently showed the resistance I felt to her entreaties, for she slipped her arm through mine and gave me the most winning of smiles. 'I am so glad you were able to come,' she continued in an excited voice, 'and that you were able to bring the umbrella. I confess that I should hardly have recognized you without it. James will be so pleased! He was sorry not to be able to meet you himself, but something cropped up at the last minute which prevented his coming, and I said I should be glad to take his place.'

"So saying, she took the umbrella gently but firmly from my grasp, and, still with her arm in mine, led me rapidly through the throng and out into the street, where the driver of a four-wheeler took my bag from me and leapt aboard his vehicle with it. For a moment I hesitated, but what was I to do? Bewildered as I was by the rapidity of events, I could see plainly enough that if I dawdled on the pavement I stood to lose both valise and umbrella, for the young lady had released my arm and was already inside the cab. Meekly, I followed her, and within seconds we were away and rattling at a furious rate up the dismal street beside the station.

"The expression on the young lady's face was tense and thoughtful, and several times she put her head to the window and glanced with a furrowed brow at the road behind us. When I attempted to do likewise, however, she suddenly and abruptly engaged me in conversation.

"'It is some time since you have been to London, is it not?' she asked, in a light, distracted voice.

"'Indeed,' I replied; 'several weeks.'

"'Very good,' said she, in a tone which indicated very clearly that she had not paid the slightest attention to my reply. I tried again to see what it was behind us that filled her with such anxiety, but she quickly spoke again and prevented it. 'Mother will be so pleased you have arrived,' said she with forced gaiety.

"'Mother?'

"'Did James not tell you? The whole family is to be there to greet you. We would not miss it for the world, as you can imagine. We have so much to tell you, and you, no doubt, have much to tell us, too.'

"I confess I knew not what to make of this prattle. Although the young lady was evidently Chambers's sister, her manner was quite unlike his, and I was beginning to wish I had never left home, when she abruptly leaned from the window of the cab and called something to the driver. Seizing the opportunity, I looked quickly from the window on my side, back the way we had come. The road was quiet, and almost deserted, but some fifty yards behind us was a hansom cab. At that distance I could not be certain, but it seemed to me that it had but one occupant, a man with a low, round hat, and a great black beard.

"At that moment, our cab lurched suddenly round a corner and I was flung back into my seat. We had passed through an area I did not know at all, and had now turned into a broad, quiet thoroughfare of handsome modern villas, which led into an attractive square. Along the side of this we rattled, at a terrifying speed, then suddenly pulled up with such abruptness that I was flung onto the floor of the cab, at my companion's feet. She threw open the door, stepped over me and leapt down, taking the umbrella with her.

"'Oh, do come quickly!' she cried in great earnest.

"So affecting was her tone that I scrambled after her obediently, and with absolutely no regard for my dignity. The cabman thereupon threw down my bag with such excessive violence that it struck me a terrific blow on the chest and quite knocked the wind out of me, but I still retained sufficient wit to look back along the road as she hurried me through a gateway, and I saw that, not forty yards away, our pursuer had stopped, and was apparently watching us. Who could this black-bearded villain be, I wondered? Into what dark and evil feud had I unwittingly intruded? Clearly the man in the hansom was an enemy of my new acquaintance, but what could have occurred, that we were pursued so remorselessly in broad daylight?

"We hurried up the short garden path to the house, and, breathless as I was, I felt a flood of relief wash over me at the sight of its stout and imposing front door. Once inside, we should be safe, I felt sure, and all would be explained to me. All at once, however, when we were almost at the door, my companion turned aside and scurried down a short flight of stone steps to a lower path. Puzzled, I nevertheless followed her, and as I did so I observed with surprise that the windows of the house were uncurtained, and thickly smeared with dirt. Clearly the house was unoccupied, and had been so for some time.

"In a moment we had reached a side gate. She unlatched it hurriedly, and we passed through, into a long back garden. Without pausing for breath, we continued our headlong flight, she tripping lightly ahead, the front of her skirts gripped tightly in her hand, I puffing and panting with my heavy bag in the rear. Through a decayed and desolate vegetable-patch we ran, beside a stable, through a second gateway, and out into a narrow, grass-grown cobbled lane. Still our hectic progress was not complete, for with neither a check in her stride nor a word to me, she hurried off again up the lane, and I followed, some yards in the rear. A cab came into view at the head of the lane, where it met the street; she called out, and the driver reined in his horse, although it seemed to me that he was stopping before ever she called to him. She opened the cab-door and climbed quickly in, and as I plunged through the open doorway after her, I recognized that the driver was the very same man who had dropped us off just round the corner, scarcely a minute before.

"'Drive on!' she cried, and away we raced, rocking wildly from side to side, until we reached a busy main road. Here the traffic was dense, and our rate of progress thus much reduced, but this did not seem to worry the young lady, whose face was flushed as much with triumph and exultation as with exertion, so it seemed to me. She still glanced at the road behind us from time to time, but her brow was unfrowning, and a smile played about her lips."

"The bearded man did not pursue you further?" queried Holmes.

Barclay shook his head.

"I never saw him again. We had evidently given him the slip. 'Well,' said I to my companion, when my breath was quite restored, 'I little thought when I left home today that I should have such an adventure!' I spoke with a jollity which I did not really feel, for I wished to indicate my friendship, in the hope that I might learn more of this mysterious and distressing business.

"For a moment she smiled silently at me, but when at last she spoke, her response stunned me like a blow on the head, so that my mind reeled, and my eyes seemed to blur.

"'I should think not,' said she gaily. 'I doubt that such things occur very often in Lincoln, Mr. Thompson!'

"'"Thompson"?' I returned. 'Did you say "Thompson"?'

"'Why, yes. You are, are you not, Mr. Thaddeus Thompson, of Tofts House, Lincoln?'

"'I most certainly am not!' I cried, attempting to rise to my feet.

"She called to the cabman, who reined in his horse and pulled in to the side of the road. The expression on her face was one of utter mortification.

"'My dear sir,' said she in a subdued voice. 'There seems to have been some dreadful mistake. I went to the station to meet my brother's old school chum, who once bounced me upon his knee when I was scarcely old enough to walk. Do you mean to tell me that you are not that man, and that you do not remember little Effie?'

"'My name is Barclay,' said I, feeling more than a little annoyed at the situation in which I found myself. 'I have never in my life known anyone by the name of Thompson, nor, for that matter, anyone called Effie!'

"'But you carried Thaddy's umbrella. He said in his letter that he would carry a bright umbrella, so that we might recognize him easily; for it is a long time since he has been to see us, and he feared, he said, that he had changed so considerably in the intervening years that the Weatheralls would find him a stranger. It is very difficult to persuade him to leave Lincoln, you know.'

"'Is it indeed?' I remarked with some asperity. 'The umbrella is my property, I can assure you, madam. I am bringing it for a friend.'

"I put out my hand and she gave me the umbrella, but with some reluctance, so it seemed to me.

"'Well,' said she. 'We are at Camden Town station, sir, so I will alight and trouble you no more. I regret very much that this mistake has occurred, but I must say that it has been a pleasure to meet you, however brief our acquaintance has been.'

"She spoke so sweetly, and with such an expression of kindness upon her face, that I felt my annoyance quite melt away. I returned her compliments, but insisted that I should be the one to alight and take the train. I stepped from the cab, it rattled quickly away, and I breathed a deep sigh of relief that the matter was at an end. These strange people, with their mysterious and sinister ways, were not connected with my friend, Chambers, after all. I did worry for a moment for the lady's safety, but she seemed well able to take care of herself, and, in any case, she had with her the cabman, who seemed something of an ally. What the mystery was which surrounded her, I could not imagine. She had offered no confidences on the matter, and I had not pressed her to any."

"It is a remarkable tale," said Sherlock Holmes, as our visitor finished speaking. "It is both interesting and suggestive. I am most grateful that you have shared it with us."

"I had no desire ever to share it with anyone," returned Barclay without enthusiasm. "I am not much of a man for mysteries, Mr. Holmes, and should have quite forgotten the matter except that it meant I had missed my friend."

"Quite so," said Holmes, nodding his head with a smile. "Pray continue, then, Mr. Barclay."

"I bought a ticket at the station, intending to return to King's Cross, or as near to it as the train would take me, in the hope that Chambers would be there still, waiting for me. I boarded the wrong train, however, and did not discover my error until I was somewhere on the other side of Hampstead. This set me back a further forty minutes, and when I finally arrived at King's Cross, Chambers was nowhere to be seen.

"Not knowing his address, I was for a while at a loss to know what to do, but then it occurred to me that I could probably discover his address from one of the friends we had in common. I immediately called into the telegraph office and wired everyone I could think of. The replies came back promptly enough, but were utterly disappointing: no one knew his address, and that ass, Lord Steeples, even went so far as to deny having ever heard of either of us. My own resources being at an end, I sought advice, and someone gave me your name, Mr. Holmes." He paused. "My only thought at first was to locate my friend, but now, as I have narrated the whole matter to you, it begins to strike me in a more suspicious light: I wonder now if the secrecy surrounding Chambers's whereabouts is purely coincidental, or if in fact he and the girl are somehow in league against me, although to what end, I confess I cannot imagine."

"There are indeed some curious and striking features in your story," said Holmes, reaching for his pipe. "A number of possible explanations suggest themselves, of course. When you were sending your wires, did you send one to your own house, in case Chambers had left any message there for you?"

"There would have been no point, for the house is empty. I have given Mrs. Dempster, my housekeeper, the weekend off, and she has gone to visit relatives of hers in Northamptonshire."

"Had you ever seen Chambers before the evening when you conversed so amicably together at Lord Steeples's house?"

"I think I may have seen him somewhere, but only at a distance; I had never before spoken to him."

"If I might make a suggestion," I ventured, "it seems to me that far from being in league, Chambers and this young woman who calls herself Effie might in fact be opposed to each other in some enterprise."

"Why so, Watson?"

"For one thing, she whisked Mr. Barclay away from the station before he had had a chance to see if Chambers were there or not; for another, she seemed keen to get hold of the umbrella – which belongs to Chambers – and reluctant to part with it when once she had it."

"Yes," said our visitor. "That is true. I had not looked at the matter in that way, I confess. In that case, the man following in the hansom might have been an agent of Chambers's, and the charming young woman sitting beside me the real villain in the matter."

"But she does not appear to have acted in a very villainous manner," observed Holmes, a slight smile playing about his lips. "Oddly, yes; even bizarrely; but not, from your account, with any great evil in her heart."

"Perhaps, unlikely as it may sound," I suggested, "Mr. Barclay has stumbled accidentally into the activities of some kind of criminal gang, and perhaps there is some secret concealed in the umbrella which is of vital importance to them. That would explain the woman's great interest in the umbrella, and why the man in the hansom was following them."

"It is certainly a singular thing," returned Holmes, smiling, "that a weekend guest should forget to take such a bright object as this umbrella home with him, and the matter becomes doubly curious when the umbrella is found wedged behind a wardrobe."

"Are you suggesting," said Barclay, "that he left it at my house on purpose?"

"That is certainly one reading of the matter. But there are great difficulties for your theory, Watson, the chief being that the woman did not in the end keep the umbrella, but seemed content to let Mr. Barclay walk off with it. I assume from your account, Mr. Barclay, that she would have had no opportunity to remove anything which might have been concealed within the umbrella?"

Our visitor shook his head. "I had the thing in view the whole time," said he, "and it was never unfastened."

Holmes frowned for a moment, then with a dry chuckle he leaned from his chair, picked up the umbrella and passed it to me. "Let us not deny ourselves the pleasure of examining the thing, then," said he.

I unfastened the clasp, and opened the umbrella out; I turned it upside down, shook it and examined it fully, but to my disappointment, there was nothing within. I rolled it up again, and we sat for some time in silence, while Holmes, with his eyes closed, and puffing slowly on his pipe, considered the matter. Then, abruptly, our visitor spoke:

"I have had a disturbing thought," said he in a quiet voice. "It has just occurred to me that I may have been deliberately lured to London so that my house can be burgled in my absence. My collection of prints is extremely valuable."

"Great Heavens!" I cried. "Such a possibility had not occurred to me!"

"But it had occurred to me," said Holmes drily, opening his eyes. "Indeed, the possibility of such a scheme was one of the very first explanations I considered. But it occurred to me with equal rapidity that the very last thing which the perpetrator of such a scheme would desire is that his victim's suspicions be aroused in any way. The ideal state of affairs from a burglar's point of view, would be for Mr. Barclay to spend a perfectly ordinary weekend away, in peace and quiet. Instead of this, however, he is subjected to such a series of alarms and perplexities, immediately upon his arrival in London, that it would have been no more than natural had he returned home there and then, which is the last effect any aspiring burglar would wish to achieve, as I am sure you would agree. Fortunately," Holmes added with a twinkle in his eye, "Mr. Barclay did not return home, but chose the more sensible course, and consulted me."

"And yet it is still just possible, is it not," I persisted, "however unlikely it may be, that burglary is indeed the motive behind it all?"

Holmes laughed. "Really, Watson, you are becoming as tenacious in your grip on a theory as our old friend, Inspector Lestrade. But, yes," he conceded, putting down his pipe, and rising to his feet, "one would have to allow that it is barely, logically, possible – in London all things are possible – despite the fact that Chambers could scarcely have done more to ensure that suspicion would fall upon him immediately should anything happen to Mr. Barclay's collection; despite the fact that Effie's efforts to keep Mr. Barclay occupied flagged after only half an hour, when there are dozens of perfectly elementary ruses which she could have adopted to keep him busy for the rest of the day; despite the fact that the burglary theory provides no adequate explanation of the bearded fellow in the hansom, the pre-meditated detour through the garden of the empty house, and the odd instructions concerning the railway stations; despite all these considerations, it is, I admit, just possible that Chambers, or someone else, intends to burgle 'The Poplars.' Perhaps the best thing, then, to set Mr. Barclay's mind at ease on the matter, would be for you to take him down to see our friend, Inspector Bradstreet. Explain to him that you are concerned about a possible burglary, Mr. Barclay – I should not trouble him with all the details – and he will make contact with the Bedfordshire force and get an officer sent out to your house at once. Will that suffice?"

"And what will you do, Mr. Holmes?"

"No more questions for the moment, Mr. Barclay, if you please. Time is slipping away as we sit here talking. If you will call back at seven o'clock this evening, I think we may have some positive news for you." He had been drawing on his overcoat as he spoke, and now, with a glance at his watch and a brisk nod to his client, he was away, his footsteps clattering rapidly down the stair. I suggested to Mr. Barclay that he might leave his bag and umbrella in our chambers for the time being, a plan with which he was very willing to comply, and a few minutes later we descended to the street and hailed a cab to take us to the police station.

At half past six that evening, I was reading the evening paper by the fireside; but there was little of interest in it, and my thoughts soon strayed back to the strange story we had heard earlier in the day. I could make no sense of it at all, and was inclined to conclude that the bizarre events in which Horace Barclay had found himself an unwilling participant were, in truth, quite unconnected, when my eye fell on the green umbrella, leaning up against the sofa, and I found myself wondering if it might not, after all, contain some secret which we had missed earlier. It could do no harm to have another look. I opened it up and subjected both the inside and the handle to a careful examination for several minutes, but found nothing hidden there, nor any place where anything could previously have been hidden. I was just about to close it up again when my eye was caught by the small white label which bore the manufacturer's name. Beneath this name a pair of initials, presumably those of the owner, had been written with an indelible pencil. These initials, however, were not those of James Chambers, but were, to my unutterable amazement, 'H B', the initials of Holmes's client, Horace Barclay.

I was still staring at the label in stupefaction, unable to comprehend what it might mean, when my thoughts were disturbed by a sudden sharp ring at the door-bell. To my surprise, a rough-looking man was shown in a moment later by the maid. His name, he said, was George Milburn, and he had come in response to a message left by a Mr. Sherlock Holmes at the cab office at King's Cross, promising half a sovereign for information about a certain fare he had had earlier that day. As I had had no word from Holmes as to when he might return, I decided to conduct the interview myself. I judged that I was sufficiently familiar with my friend's methods to extract any information which the man might have, although, in the event, this amounted to very little.

He worked, he said, out of Woodham's Yard, King's Cross. It was outside that station that he had been hailed that morning by a well-dressed young woman with curly blonde hair, who had instructed him to wait at the side-entrance and be ready for an immediate and rapid departure when she returned. She had given him a sovereign, and told him that there would be another for him if he followed her instructions precisely. He was to drive with all speed to a certain house in Camden Square, where she and her companion would alight, then to wait round the corner, at the head of a lane, until they re-emerged, whereupon he was to make for Camden Town as fast as possible.

So far his testimony merely confirmed the story of Holmes's client, without adding any fresh information, although it did establish for certain that the young woman had foreseen the pursuit which took place, and had planned the route in advance, including the detour through the garden of the empty house.

"Where did the young lady finally alight?" I asked.

"Corner of Camden High Street and Crowndale Road," he replied; "about a quarter mile after the gentleman."

This information made it certain that the woman had made no attempt to return to King's Cross station, so that the story she had told Mr. Barclay, of having gone there to meet a Mr. Thompson from Lincoln, was therefore a complete falsehood. I handed the cabman the half-sovereign, and was about to dismiss him, when there came the sound of rapid footsteps upon the stair. A moment later the door flew open and Holmes hurried into the room. The cabman quickly repeated his scanty information.

"Did you observe in which direction she walked after she had alighted?" Holmes asked when the man had finished.

"She crossed the road towards Mornington Crescent, sir."

Holmes nodded. "And no doubt she was wearing gloves?"

"Yes, sir. Grey cotton."

"Hum. Perhaps she removed them when she was paying you?"

"Yes, sir; that's exactly what she did."

"Ah! And as she did so, you observed upon her left hand a wedding-ring, and also another, jewelled ring, with a dark stone in the centre, and half a dozen small diamonds around the edge."

"'Pon my word, sir! You have described the ring exactly!"

"Thank you," said Holmes with a smile of satisfaction. "You can always rely on a jarvey to observe jewellery, Watson," he remarked when, with a little salute, the man had left us, a broad grin upon his face. "After a while they become quite skilled at assessing the worth of their customers from such little details." He had been rummaging in the drawer of his desk as he spoke, and now he took from it his revolver, and slipped it into the pocket of his overcoat. "Now," said he, glancing at the clock, "there is time, I think, for a stirrup cup. Let us take something warming, then, before venturing out once more into this chilly evening!"

"Where are you going?"

"To pay a call on James Chambers. Will you come?"

"Certainly, if you wish it. Do you anticipate danger?"

"Events sometimes take a surprising turn," said he after a moment, in a considered tone. "You will recall the arrest of Mary Monteith, no doubt? The pistol is a precaution, Watson; that is all. I should be obliged if you did not mention it to Mr. Barclay. It might alarm him. But, unless I am much mistaken, that is our client's cab outside now. If you would be so good as to bring the gamp and bag, we can be off."

"One moment, Holmes," said I, as I remembered my recent discovery. I quickly told him of the label inside the umbrella. "It bears the initials–"

"'H B', I should imagine," my friend interrupted.

I confess I was stunned with surprise. "How on earth do you know that?" I cried.

"It is as I thought," said he simply. "Perhaps, Watson," he added in a thoughtful voice, "you could enquire about those initials when I give you a sign."

I threw on my coat, and, picking up the umbrella and Mr. Barclay's bag, hurried after Holmes as he ran downstairs. A moment later, we had joined his client in the cab and were rattling away through the darkened streets. Barclay sat huddled in the corner, his eyes unhopeful and his expression one of fatigue. Holmes, by contrast, was alert and vibrant with barely suppressed energy. His eyes glittered, and his whole face seemed sharpened and thrust forward, like an excited hound who has the scent in his nostrils and is impatient to be off the leash.

"You spoke to Inspector Bradstreet, I take it?" said he, when we had gone some way.

"Indeed," Barclay replied. "He was most helpful, as were the Bedfordshire Police. They were soon able to inform us that there had been no untoward occurrences at 'The Poplars,' and no strangers had been seen in the neighbourhood; but they say they will keep the house under observation, nevertheless."

Holmes nodded his head. "Now," said he, "to explain matters to you: I have found Mr. Chambers, although, in truth, he was scarcely lost. It had struck me that a man with a knowledge of old prints sufficient for him to be able to engage such an authority as you in conversation, Mr. Barclay, might well be known to the London dealers, and so it proved. Half an hour with a trade directory, followed by a few enquiries at picture-galleries and sale-rooms, gave me the information I required. In truth, I was almost disappointed at the ease with which the facts fell into my lap; it was as if a mountaineer who has prepared himself for an arduous and difficult climb discovers before he has gone ten paces that there exists an easy path to the summit, up which he can stroll without effort. Of course, there is a lesson in everything if we care to take it," he added with a dry chuckle, "and the lesson of this is clearly that satisfaction comes not from the end achieved, but from the struggle to reach that end.

"What I discovered," he continued after a moment, "is that Chambers himself has an interest in a small gallery in Davies Street, which trades under the name of Lambert.

There is an extremely garrulous young assistant there, who seemed to have nothing better to do than answer my questions, and I was soon able to learn Chambers's home address, which is in Highbury Fields, and also most of his life history and that of his immediate relations, which is not, I might add, in the first rank from the point of view of general interest."

It was clear that Holmes was not inclined to say more for the moment, and I did not press him. As for his client, he seemed to have settled into a state of passive acceptance of whatever Fate might have in store for him. He and I had earlier passed a pleasant half-hour, while waiting at the police station, in discussing the history of racing; and although I did not know the direction his thoughts had taken since then, it was clear from every line on his face that his spirits had fallen somewhat, and that he wished he had never left his home that morning. The cab rattled on in the darkness, as I pondered further the curious circumstances surrounding his arrival in London, past the great bulk of the buildings along the Euston Road, through Pentonville, and so on towards Islington. The night was very clear, and bitterly cold, and the dark and gloomy streets were almost deserted. Only the noisy and brightly-lit public houses at the street-corners gave any indication that there throbbed a hidden, persistent life beneath the darkened and forbidding exterior of the city. Of Mr. Barclay's adventure I could make nothing, and nor was I very hopeful that in finding Chambers we should get to the bottom of it. Probably, Chambers had simply tired of waiting for his friend at King's Cross, and was as mystified as to his whereabouts now as his friend had been mystified about him; and perhaps the woman Barclay had encountered was indeed some kind of monomaniac, inhabiting a world of her own imagination. Perhaps she made a habit of meeting trains at King's Cross, and subjected a new victim each day to her strange ways. But there were certain features of the matter which I could not so easily explain away in this fashion, and I was still pondering the problem without having reached any conclusion when we turned at last into Highbury Terrace.

Chambers's house lay in the middle of a long, tall, flat-fronted row, which faced onto a large, open square in which I could just make out the shadowed shapes of trees. Darkened, and in complete silence, the house presented a cold and unwelcoming appearance, and I feared that our journey might even yet prove a fruitless one. Eventually our ring at the bell was answered, however, and a young girl showed us into a pleasant, tastefully decorated drawing-room at the rear of the house. Pictures and bric-a-brac of all kinds were displayed upon the walls and upon every available surface, and over all there was an air of solidity and permanence, and certainly no indication of any recent domestic upheaval, such as Chambers had mentioned in his letters to Mr. Barclay. But for the crackle of the fire blazing in the grate, and the ticking of a clock on the mantelpiece, all was silent and still, although, as we stood there, the faint, distant sound of voices came to my ear, and somewhere above us a door closed softly. Moments later, the door of the drawing-room was opened, to admit a tall young man with wavy hair and round, ruddy features.

"My dear Barclay!" he cried, rushing up to his friend and wringing his hand vigorously. "How very glad I am to see you! I had quite given you up, I am afraid. But who are these gentlemen?"

"This is Mr. Holmes and Dr. Watson, who have assisted me in finding you when my own efforts had proved unavailing."

"Thank goodness you were able to help," said Chambers, shaking us both by the hand. "You will take a sherry, gentlemen?" He rang for the maid. "I waited at King's Cross for over an hour and a half, Barclay, and met twenty-three trains before I gave it up. Then I sent a wire to your house, but it was returned to me undelivered. They said there was no one there to receive it. I could not think where you had got to! When did you arrive in London?"

"At twelve-forty-seven, as we had arranged," returned Barclay, appearing a little uncomfortable. "But I was distracted. I had a slight adventure, which took me away from the station, and I did not get back for two hours. I'll tell you about it later."

"Well, well!" said Chambers, clapping him on the shoulder. "All's well that ends well, eh?"

"Yes, thank goodness," said Barclay with a sigh of relief.

"And I see that you found the umbrella, too–"

"One moment," interrupted Holmes. His tone was authoritative and cold, and the other two men looked at him in surprise, the smiles frozen upon their faces. "I am not satisfied."

"Excuse me," said Chambers in a testy voice, "but I don't understand."

"I am not satisfied with your account, nor with your conduct towards my client."

"I do not see that it is your place to express dissatisfaction," returned Chambers, a note of anger in his voice. "You have assisted Mr. Barclay in finding me, and you have manifestly succeeded. I'll ring for the maid to show you out."

"You will do no such thing," said Holmes coldly; "for if you do, the matter will be placed in the hands of the police within half an hour."

A look of alarm came into Chambers's eyes. "How dare you threaten me!" he cried in a blustering voice. "Your part in the matter is at an end."

"We wish," said I boldly, in response to a slight sign from Holmes, "to know about the initials 'H B.'"

The two men looked at one another. "What are you talking about?" said Chambers in a strained voice. "Why, this is 'H B' – Mr. Horace Barclay!"

"There is another," said Holmes, taking the umbrella from me: "the owner of this." He tossed the umbrella onto the floor. "His initials are on the label."

There was a moment of utter silence, in which Holmes remained perfectly motionless, Barclay's features assumed a look of complete stupefaction, and Chambers's eyes darted about the room, as he clenched and unclenched his hands spasmodically. Again I thought I heard slight sounds from outside the room: soft footsteps, and the creaking of a floor-board.

"The umbrella was not new when I acquired it," said Chambers at length, in a breathless tone. "'H B' must have been a previous owner–"

"Do not waste our time further, Mr. Chambers," said Holmes. "Do you recall the Stillingfleet case, Mr. Barclay? – about four years ago, in Croydon?"

"The name means nothing to me, I'm afraid."

"No? It created quite a sensation at the time, I remember. A Dr. Alfred Stillingfleet murdered his wife and buried her body in the garden. Shortly afterwards, her relatives became suspicious when they failed to receive the usual letters from her, for she had previously been a prolific correspondent, and they therefore hired a private enquiry agent to watch the house. Stillingfleet, however, quickly became aware of this fellow, who was a singularly incompetent operator by all accounts, and he therefore arranged for his maid, who had been his partner in the crime, to dress in such a way as to impersonate his late wife and parade up and down the streets of the district until the agent went away satisfied, and wrote his erroneously reassuring report. By this ruse, which was repeated from time to time, and by the forging of letters, Stillingfleet was able to postpone the discovery of the crime for almost two years."

"It is an unpleasant and distressing story," said Barclay; "but I fail to see its relevance."

"It is by no means unique. There was a similar case in Brussels two years ago, and an almost identical one in Hamburg just last year. I believe that the man with the beard who followed you this morning was almost certainly a detective, and as it is apparent for various reasons, including the evidence we have heard from the cabman, that the woman you were with fully expected to be followed from the station, it seems likely that her every action was performed with this man in mind."

"But to what end? And, in any case, what have I to do with those people?"

"If you will consider the matter for a moment, it will surely be obvious to you," returned Holmes, a trace of impatience in his voice. "What does this woman do first? She makes a great, unnecessary scene at the station, thus drawing the attention of everyone there to the fact that she has met you. She then hurries away with you and shakes off the pursuit by a simple but ingenious ruse. Clearly she wishes you to be seen, but not too closely; she wishes anyone who is interested – which means the man with the beard – to know that you have left the station in her company, but not that you have later parted in Camden Town."

"But why, Mr. Holmes, why?" cried Barclay, a look of utter bewilderment upon his face. "Why should anyone wish to see me, or see where I go?"

"Because, Mr. Barclay, that person wished to be certain that you were who he thought you were."

"And who on earth did he think I was, then?"

"Let us suppose for the sake of argument that this woman, 'Effie,' has done away with her husband, and has so far managed to allay the suspicions of his relatives and friends by telling them that he is out of town for a while. The day will arrive, sooner or later, when she must produce him once more, especially if she knows she is being watched by a hired detective. If she has a suitable male confederate, there will be no problem. But let us further suppose that she has no suitable confederate. What is she to do? Clearly she must find some stranger who can pass, at a distance, for her husband. Do I make myself clear?"

Barclay nodded glumly, but the puzzled expression never left his face. "So you believe that everything which that strange woman told me was untrue?"

"I am certain of it. And the purpose of the umbrella, which Mr. Chambers deliberately left at your house, so that you would have to bring it with you–"

"Oh, this is preposterous!" cried Chambers, who had been standing in silence all the time Holmes had been speaking. "I have listened to enough of this nonsense!" He stepped to the bell-pull, a determined expression on his face. But before his hand had touched it, the door of the room burst open, and a pretty, blonde-haired young woman swept into the room with a swishing of her indigo silk evening-dress.

Horace Barclay took a quick step backwards, and raised his arm as if to fend her off. "You!" he cried, a look of stunned recognition in his eyes.

"Violet!" cried Chambers, in a tone of alarm.

"It is no use, James," said she in a firm voice. "I have been listening outside the door. These gentlemen have somehow discovered our little ruse, and now suspect us of something far worse than the truth. We have little enough to be ashamed of. We must tell them all, so that they can understand the position in which I found myself. Pray, take a seat, gentlemen," she continued, turning to us, as Chambers himself sat down heavily in a chair by the fire, like a man finally admitting defeat. "I will explain everything. But first I must ask you a question, and I must beg of you that on your honour as gentlemen you will answer me truthfully."

I nodded my head, mystified as to what she might be going to ask us.

"Are you," said she, "in the employment of Lord Crosspool?"

"Lord Crosspool?" said Holmes in surprise. "The gentleman who was brought before the magistrates a couple of years ago for discharging a fowling-piece at the local rector? I seem to recall that he insisted upon being tried by the House of Lords until persuaded that he was merely making an ass of himself; but, other than that, I know nothing of the man."

"I have never even heard of him," said I.

For a moment she looked keenly into our eyes, then, evidently satisfied, she nodded her head.

"Very well," said she. "I will tell you all. But do not blame James, I implore you! My brother acted only to help me. He had wanted no part in the matter, and only became involved because I begged him."

I glanced over to where Chambers sat by the fire, his elbows upon the arms of the chair, his head sunk in his hands.

"My maiden name was Violet Chambers," she continued. "Eighteen months ago, however, I was married, and became Mrs. Henry Beauchamp. At that time my husband had recently completed his studies at Oxford. He is the second son of Lord Crosspool, of Crosspool Park, Shropshire. To his elder brother, Ronald, will naturally devolve in due course all the duties and privileges of the estate, and it was the wish of Lord Crosspool that Henry's career be made in the local regiment, the Shropshire Fusiliers, in which Lord Crosspool himself had served as a young man. But Henry's inclinations have always been elsewhere, and this has led to considerable friction between them, I am afraid. Henry's great interest is in the ancient world, and he wishes to devote his energies to archaeology. Lord Crosspool has scarcely left his estates all his life, and his views are very narrow and rigid. He sees no merit in Henry's ambitions at all, and he absolutely forbade him to speak of the matter again, on pain of being utterly disowned, cut off completely from his family, without a penny to his name. What was my husband to do? In a year's time, so he had every reason to believe, he would be able to secure an excellent position at the British Museum, but for the moment he was entirely dependent upon his father for his livelihood. He begged for a little time in which to consider his future, and to continue for the moment his education in London, to which request Lord Crosspool eventually, with extreme reluctance, assented.

"Then, late last August, Henry was offered the chance of joining an archaeological expedition to Egypt, under the guidance of Flinders Petrie. He had to make a decision quickly, as the opportunity had only arisen because of another man's incapacity through illness, and the party was to leave in a few days. All one night he stayed awake, considering the proposition from every aspect. At length, in the morning, when I told him that it was my wish that he should go, he made his decision. He left England on the fifth of September last year, and has spent the winter at Karnak, on the Nile. He has written regularly to me, and it has been a source of great pleasure to me to hear of the great work he is doing, and the experience he has gained. Now, in his last letter but one, he informs me that he has been offered a post on the research staff of the Museum, to begin in June, so that it seems our future is at last assured.

"All this time, it was essential that his father did not learn that he was away from England. There seemed little difficulty in this at first, for Lord Crosspool rarely comes to London; but one Saturday in February some matter concerning the estate had brought him up to town to see his legal advisers, and he arrived quite unannounced at our little house in Mornington Road, where I was quite alone. On the spur of the moment, I told him that Henry was away for a few days, visiting an old college friend in York, and he seemed at first to be satisfied with that explanation for Henry's absence. But something must have aroused his suspicious nature, for I discovered later that he had questioned the servants closely when I was not present. I do not believe he learned anything definite from them, but two weeks later a man with a black beard, piercing eyes, and the smell of beer about him called at the house. He gave his name as O'Donnell, and said he had some confidential information for my husband, which he was obliged to deliver personally, and he asked me when Henry would be returning. I did not believe his story, and suspected that he was an agent of my father-in-law's, and this suspicion was in some measure confirmed when I subsequently saw him loitering in the street at odd times of the day, with a note-book in his hand. No doubt he would soon be reporting back to Lord Crosspool that Henry was nowhere to be seen. What could I do? I was sure that if Henry were here to explain matters to his father, all might still be well. But if his father discovered the truth while Henry was absent and thus unable to defend himself, Lord Crosspool might in his rage carry out what he had threatened. Henry was to leave Alexandria in two weeks' time, but by then it might be too late, the damage might already have been done. If only there were some way I could convince the investigator that Henry was here, in London!"

"I do not see that any further deception was necessary," interrupted Sherlock Holmes. "Your husband's father could hardly take any decisive step unless he knew for certain that his son was abroad, and how could he learn that?"

"Oh, if only I had had your advice before, sir," Mrs. Beauchamp responded after a moment. "I see now that you are right. As it was, I saw then only that ruin awaited us unless I could throw Lord Crosspool's detective off the scent! It was as I was pondering the matter, in my agitation, that I remembered James's telling me of an odd coincidence. A gentleman he had met recently, he said, not only had the same initials as my husband, but bore a strong resemblance to him, from a distance at least. That gentleman was Mr. Barclay, and I found myself wondering, as I recalled James's words, if it might be possible to pass Mr. Barclay off as my husband. I put it to James, and his first reaction was to utterly reject the idea as preposterous; but gradually I managed to convince him that it might work, so long as this man, O'Donnell, did not get too close a look at Mr. Barclay, and would harm no one. In the end, reluctantly, he agreed to it.

"The plan, then, was that James would invite Mr. Barclay to London, where I would meet him in such a way as to convince Mr. O'Donnell – who I knew would be following me – that he was my husband. In order to make it appear as if Henry were returning from York, we had somehow to arrange it so that the meeting occurred at King's Cross Station, which is where the express trains from Yorkshire arrive, and, as a final touch, it was contrived, as you have no doubt realised, that Mr. Barclay would be carrying Henry's umbrella. It is an article which anyone who knows Henry would instantly associate with him. He has had it for years, and takes it everywhere, and I thought that if Lord Crosspool's spy mentioned the umbrella in his report it would make it seem conclusive. The intention was that we should give Mr. O'Donnell the slip, and then part, so that Mr. Barclay could return in the cab to King's Cross, where James would be waiting for him. Unfortunately, I had not thought the matter through sufficiently, and I had not foreseen that Mr. Barclay is too much of a gentleman to have remained in the cab while I alighted, but would insist upon being the one to alight. Alas! He was somehow delayed, and although James waited for nearly two hours, it was not enough! James has been beside himself with concern for his friend ever since. I, meanwhile, returned straight home to learn from the maid that another stranger, a tall man whose name she did not catch, had been asking for me earlier this afternoon. Suspecting another of Lord Crosspool's spies, I left Mornington Road at once and came straight here to my brother's, to avoid being seen alone. There! Now you know everything."

As she finished her account, delivered in a rapid, breathless tone, her breast was heaving with emotion. There followed a long silence. At length, Sherlock Holmes spoke.

"It is an interesting story, madam," said he, "illustrative of the truth that one lie leads on to another, and that what begins as a small deception frequently ends as a very great one. If what you say is true, then, at the very least, you owe Mr. Barclay the most profound apology; but is it true? How are we to judge? You have already today given one demonstration of your abilities as an actress, and you will therefore understand if we now hesitate before granting you our full credence."

The lady bit her lower lip, and put her hands to her face.

"What I have told you is the truth," said she after a moment in a quiet voice; "although I can hardly blame you for your incredulity. I know I cannot expect your forgiveness, although I am sincerely sorry for the trouble my schemes have caused, so I ask only your belief. One moment!" she cried abruptly, as an idea struck her. "Perhaps you could show these gentlemen the press-cuttings, James."

Her brother nodded eagerly, and hurried from the room. In a minute he was back, bearing a small sheaf of papers in his hand.

"Here are a couple of letters which Henry has sent me from Egypt," said he, "and this is a scrap-book I have been keeping."

He opened the latter near the beginning, and showed us a newspaper cutting, dated the sixth of September, 1887, which described the embarkation of the Egyptian Archaeological Party, in which the name of Henry Beauchamp was mentioned.

"Will his father not have seen this report, or a similar one?" I queried.

Mrs. Beauchamp shook her head. "There is little fear of that," she returned. "He reads nothing, except *The Field*, and military and naval reports."

Sherlock Holmes sifted through the papers for some moments, then he looked up, tapping his fingers on the pile before him, and gazed steadily into the lady's eyes. "If we agree to let the matter rest here for the moment," said he at length, "you must bring your husband to see us upon his return. What say you, Watson?"

I nodded my assent, and was about to speak, when Barclay rose to his feet, and cleared his throat.

"Whatever is decided about *that*," said he in a stiff voice, "my position here is clearly a false one. It seems that I have served my purpose, so if you will ask your servant to summon a cab, I will trouble you no more."

"No, no, my dear fellow," cried Chambers, putting out his arms as if he would physically prevent the other man from leaving the room. "I would not have you go for the world! If our foolish plots should cause a rift between us, I should never forgive myself!"

"You can hardly suppose that it is of any moment to me whether you choose to forgive yourself or not," returned Barclay coldly. "I have been used most despicably."

"We did not think–" began Mrs. Beauchamp, her face the very picture of regret; but the severity of Horace Barclay's expression evidently deterred her, for she broke off, and did not complete the sentence.

A heavy silence fell upon the room, and for several minutes there was nothing to be heard but the crackle and splutter of the fire in the grate, and the ticking of the clock above it. Then, with an abruptness which made me start from my chair, there came the fierce jangling of the front-door bell. A moment later, the maid opened the door to announce Mr. Ronald Beauchamp.

A tall, athletic-looking man strode briskly into the room. He was about thirty years of age, I judged, with large, clean-shaven features, and flaxen hair. He stepped quickly to Mrs. Beauchamp and took her hand.

"Violet!" said he. "How good it is to see you again! I've had the devil of a job finding you! I've been calling at your house all day, but your maid denied knowing where you had gone. Eventually I guessed that you might be at your brother's house. James!" he cried, turning to Chambers, and the two men exchanged greetings. "Henry not here?" he enquired, then he laughed. "I thought perhaps not. That rather explains one or two things! I've come up to town as soon as I could, especially to see you, Violet. I have something important to tell you." He glanced in our direction.

"You may speak freely before these gentlemen," said Mrs. Beauchamp.

"Very well. I discovered recently – quite by chance – that my father had employed a private detective to spy on you and Henry. Knowing what I did of Henry's plans and intentions, I guessed that it was something to do with digging, or with Egypt, or both. Well, I don't mind telling you that I told the old man precisely what I thought of his spying. I didn't mince my words, and there was a blazing row. Then, as soon as I was able to leave the estate, I hurried to warn you. So, here I am! Quite frankly, I think that having my strong disagreement made so clear to him, the old man will think again, and you may find that he is a bit more amenable to Henry's plans from now on. But, who are these gentlemen?" he continued. "They must think me terribly rude, to burst in upon your party and ignore them." He glanced round, and then his eye fell on Holmes's client, who had been standing in silence by the door all this time. At once, his eyebrows shot up in surprise. "Why, if it isn't Horace Barclay!" he cried. "Whatever are you doing here, my dear fellow? I didn't know that you were acquainted with my relations!"

Horace Barclay took a step forward and blinked in surprise.

"Bless my soul!" he cried. "Ronald Beauchamp! I'm afraid I did not recognize you, old man. When this young lady introduced herself earlier as Mrs. Beauchamp, I never thought to connect her with you!" He shook the other heartily by the hand. "This is my dear old friend, Ronald Ignatius Beauchamp," he explained, turning to us. "We were at Oxford together. Indeed, we were on the same stair at St. Matthew's for two years. It must be nearly ten years since I've seen you, Beauchamp! What a very happy chance! How have you been keeping? And how are your charming young sisters, Beth and Phyllis, who used to come with their aunt to visit us in College?"

The two men conversed gaily for several minutes, and seemed set for several hours, but Chambers interrupted them.

"You will all stay and have supper with us?" said he. Beauchamp assented with enthusiasm, but Barclay hesitated and frowned, as if endeavouring to weigh against each other several conflicting emotions.

"Oh, very well, then," said he at length, his mouth broadening into a smile. "But I insist – absolutely insist – that my old friend here hears all about this afternoon's adventure while we eat. I will recount it, and 'Effie' can correct me if I go wrong!"

"'Effie'?" queried Beauchamp in surprise.

"I will explain all over supper," said his sister-in-law, laughing.

"It is pleasing," said Holmes, rising to his feet, "that matters appear to have resolved themselves to everyone's satisfaction, for the present at least. I think, Watson," he continued, turning to me, "that we might most profitably return to Baker Street."

"You will not take a little something with us?" said Chambers.

"Thank you, but no," returned Holmes. "Our cook has promised us fowls of rare distinction this evening, so we are under some obligation to put in an appearance at the dinner table. It has been a diverting, but tiring day. Do bring your husband to see us when he returns, Mrs. Beauchamp. I have followed Flinders Petrie's work with the utmost interest, and should be pleased to have a first-hand account of the latest findings!"

Holmes was in a light-hearted mood as we returned to Baker Street, chuckling as he expressed his pleasure that his worst fears had not been realised.

"I am particularly glad that the pistol proved unnecessary," he remarked with a smile, patting the bulge in his overcoat pocket. "It may be, Watson, that my professional experience has inclined me always to expect the worst possible outcome, but I by no means welcome it, and it is indeed a delight to be mistaken for once. I must confess that when I learned from the young assistant at Chambers's gallery this afternoon that his employer had a sister whose description exactly matched that of the woman Mr. Barclay had encountered at King's Cross, I did fear the worst. It made certain, you see, what we had suspected, that the two of them were in it together. Her occasional visits to her brother's gallery had evidently left a strong impression upon his assistant, incidentally, for he was able to give me the most detailed description of her, even down to the appearance of her ring, which enabled me to confirm the matter beyond doubt with the cabman, as you saw. The assistant also informed me that she had been married the autumn before last, to a Mr. Henry Beauchamp, which is why I fully expected the initials you had found in the umbrella to be 'H B.' I seemed then to see a crime unfolding before me on the very model of the Stillingfleet case, and I think I can be forgiven for judging it so."

"Certainly," said I, "but thank Heavens you were wrong, Holmes! In fact, your reading of the deception being practised was correct in every detail; but, fortunately, in this case, there was no great evil behind it all, and no one is harmed by it. The treatment of Mr. Barclay was perhaps a little callous—"

"Oh, his pride will recover," Holmes interrupted in a gay tone, "and the story of his adventure will establish him for life at the dinner-parties of London!"

Thus ended the singular adventure of Mr. Horace Barclay. And yet, for him, it was not an end, but a beginning; for, some eighteen months later, I heard that he had married Elizabeth Beauchamp, the sister of his old college friend. Perhaps the most surprising aspect of this was that in so doing he had become related through marriage to the young blonde-haired stranger with whom he had once shared a cab in such surprising circumstances, and whom he could not have imagined he would ever see again. That lady did pay us a visit with her husband shortly after his return from Egypt, when we were pleased and interested to hear of the latest discoveries there, and to hear, also, that the disagreement between Lord Crosspool and his son had at last been resolved amicably, and that the two were reconciled once more.

A week after the events I have described, a parcel arrived one morning at our chambers in Baker Street. It contained a cheque and a letter of thanks from Horace Barclay, and also a handsome pair of matching prints, which he hoped would be of interest to us, depicting Champion's unprecedented double triumph in the Derby and St. Leger of 1800. With a chuckle, Holmes passed these to me. I accepted them gladly, and hung them that very day on the wall above the dressing-table in my bedroom, since which time they have never ceased to give me pleasure.

THE JET BROOCH

DURING THE YEARS I shared chambers with Mr. Sherlock Holmes, the well-known criminal investigator, he handled many cases which involved the intimate private concerns of families whose names would be recognized by most readers of the daily press. I have included but few of these in this series of records I have lain before the public, for obvious reasons. I would be guilty of gross indiscretion and a very great breach of confidence were I to even hint at the nature of some of these cases, let alone provide a detailed account. Occasionally, however, when some time has elapsed since the events in question, and when I am able with a few little changes to disguise the identities of those involved, it is possible for me to give an account of one or two of these cases, if I judge that the facts of the matter are of sufficient interest to warrant it. Such a case is the one I shall now recount, an odd little tangle with a mysterious package at one end and a well-known song at the other.

It was the week before Christmas. The weather was cold, and I had awoken that morning to the rapid rat-a-tat-tat of hail against my bedroom window. Our breakfast finished, Sherlock Holmes had pulled the sofa a little nearer to the fire, and now lounged there in his old mouse-coloured dressing-gown, examining a small, flat package, about an inch in depth and three or four inches square, which had been delivered that morning.

"I wonder what this can be?" he remarked, turning it over in his hand, as I sat down on the other side of the fireplace. "I was not expecting anything today, so it is probably from a stranger."

"Why do you not open it and see?" I suggested.

"All in good time," said he. "I prefer to examine the outside first. It is easier to extract any information that may be there while the package is still intact. What do you make of it, Watson?" he asked, tossing it across to me.

"It is a little lighter than I had expected," I said, weighing it in my hand. "I thought it might have been a tin of tobacco, but I don't think it is heavy enough for that. It is wrapped in rather dull brown paper. This is not gummed in any way; it is simply fastened with string. It feels as if there is a small cardboard box inside the wrapping," I added, as I gave the package a gentle squeeze.

"Anything else?"

"Not that I can see."

"The address?"

I looked again at the address. "Why," I said in surprise, "the house number has been missed off. It simply says 'Mr. Sherlock Holmes, Baker Street, London'."

"Precisely. We benefit from the fact that the postman has delivered so many letters to me in the year we have been living here that he knows where to find me even when the address is incomplete. Now, I can't imagine that anyone who knew it would forget to include the house number in the address. It therefore seems likely that it was not known by the sender, who just trusted to luck that the parcel would find me. This supports my initial supposition that it is from a stranger, and someone, moreover, who was not in a position to find out my full address. Are there any more clues in the wrapping?"

"I don't think so," I replied after a moment.

"What about the string?"

"It is just a commonplace piece of thin twine," I said as I examined it.

"Not quite," said Holmes with a shake of the head. "It is certainly commonplace, but it is not one piece but three, which have been knotted together to make a suitable length."

"That is true, but is that of any significance?"

"Well, it suggests either someone who is very parsimonious with his string – using short pieces which most people would probably have thrown away – or perhaps a servant or other employee who has used discarded string – perhaps rescued from a waste-paper basket – to avoid being accused of using his employer's property for his own purposes."

"It is possible."

"Next we come to the handwriting itself, which, as you see, is in pencil. It seems to me it is a woman's hand. Why the handwriting of men and women should differ in so distinctive a way, I do not know – it is a mystery I have not yet solved – but that they do so differ is undeniable. Of course, each hand has its own idiosyncrasies and not all women write in this way, but I have never yet encountered a single man whose hand was like this. Therefore we are probably justified in saying it is the hand of a woman. It is clear enough, but not very regularly formed, so it may be the hand of a young person, although that inference cannot be drawn with the same degree of confidence. As to what you describe as dull brown paper, I think it is simply ordinary brown paper turned back to front, with the shiny side on the inside and the dull side on the outside. This suggests someone using old paper, and accords with the inferences we drew from the knotted string. Let us now open the package and see what it contains!"

He took a small pen-knife from the little table by his elbow, neatly cut the string and slipped it from the packet. Then he unwrapped the brown paper and examined it closely for a moment. "This piece has been cut – rather hurriedly to judge from the irregular shape – from a larger sheet. It is indeed a used piece of paper, for on the other side there is another address, written in ink, in a different hand. I rather fancy that my mysterious correspondent has used this ingenious method to indicate where the package has come from."

He passed me the paper and I saw that the address on the back of it was "Sir George Datchett, 8 Cumberland Gardens, Kensington", although the name on the first line had been crossed through with a pencil. Holmes, meanwhile, was carefully lifting the lid from the cardboard box which had been wrapped in the paper. As he did so, he let out a cry of surprise, and I saw that the box was full to the brim with some white powder. He licked his finger, pushed it into the powder and tasted it.

"It is flour," said he, "perfectly ordinary flour. If you would pass me a piece of paper from the desk, Watson, I will tip it out and see if there is anything else beneath the flour."

I laid the sheet of paper on the hearth-rug and watched as my companion carefully tipped the flour onto it. All at once, a small, dark object fell out onto the little heap of flour. He picked it up, blew off the loose flour, then rubbed it on the sleeve of his dressing-gown. As he held it up, I saw that it was an ornate brooch. In the centre was a circular black disc, the size of a large coin, its surface faceted so that it caught the light with each slight movement, and around the edge was a golden rim in which the metal was teased into fantastic little twirls and curls.

"The stone in the middle looks like jet," I said.

My friend nodded his head. "Yes, and the setting is gold. It looks quite a valuable piece of jewellery." He passed me the brooch, and lifted the lid of the box to his nose. "There is a distinctive smell to this box," he said.

"Of what?"

"Soap. Scented soap. Quite expensive, I should say, as might be used in a fairly well-to-do household. Now, why should anyone send me a jet brooch without explanation, packed in flour in an old soap-box? Ah!"

He leaned over and extracted a tiny scrap of paper from the little heap of flour on the floor. The paper was of a rough, irregular shape and appeared to have been torn from the edge of a sheet of newspaper.

"Perhaps this will make things clearer," said my companion, but his face remained impassive as he examined it, and, with a frown, he passed it to me.

Upon the scrap of paper, just three words were written in pencil: "Please help me".

"That does not tell us much," I remarked.

"No," said Holmes. "It is written in the same hand as the address, and with the same pencil, but that is no more than one would expect."

"I wonder why the box has been filled with flour."

"Presumably to prevent the brooch from rattling about. The use of flour suggests someone who has access to a kitchen, or, to look at it another way, someone who does not have access to any more usual packing material, such as cotton wool. To sum up, then, our mysterious correspondent is probably female, probably young, and probably a domestic servant in a well-to-do household, who has read or heard my name somewhere and believes I may be able to help her. In what way she requires help we cannot say. It may have something to do with this brooch, but that is not certain. The brooch may be simply a deposit to secure my services – although it seems an unlikely piece of jewellery for a young housemaid to have in her possession."

"I was just thinking the same," I remarked. "It looks like something an older woman might wear."

As I was speaking there came a ring at the front doorbell. A few moments later our landlady appeared in the doorway to inform us that a lady had called to see Mr. Sherlock Holmes, but had declined to give her name.

"One moment, Mrs. Hudson," said Holmes, springing to his feet. "I shall just restore a little order, and then you can show her up." Carefully, he picked up from the floor the sheet of paper on which lay the little heap of flour and carried it over to his desk. I gathered together the brown paper, string and cardboard box and handed them to him. These, together with the brooch and scrap of paper, he also placed on his desk and closed the lid. "Now," said he, as he pulled the sofa back from the fire, "I think we are ready to receive our visitor."

The woman who was shown into our room a few moments later was tall and stately in her bearing. Although of middle age she had retained the figure and posture of a younger woman. She was wearing a very smart dark blue costume with yellow piping on the edges.

"Pray, take a seat," said Holmes, indicating the chair beside the hearth, "and let us know what we can do for you."

"No, thank you," returned our visitor in a firm tone. "I shall not be here for more than a few moments. I have simply called to collect something."

"Oh?" said Holmes in surprise. "And what might that be?"

"A brooch," said she. "My brooch. It has been sent here in error. The wrong address was written on the package."

"Did you address it yourself?"

"No. Someone else did."

"To whom should it have been sent?"

"To the jeweller. The clasp needs repairing."

"Well," said Holmes, "so far as I am aware, we have received no misaddressed parcels here."

"You must have; it was posted yesterday."

Holmes shook his head. "It is but a few days to Christmas, madam," said he, "and you must know what that means for postal deliveries. The sorting-offices have mailbags piled up to the ceiling, and everything takes longer than usual. If you would give me your name and address," he continued, taking up his note-book and pencil from the table, "I shall let you know if any misaddressed parcel arrives here."

The woman hesitated. "No," said she. "I shall call again tomorrow."

She had turned to leave us, but stopped as Holmes spoke again.

"It seems strange to me," said he, "that you should have my address at all. Do you – or anyone in your household – wish me to look into some problem for you?"

"Absolutely not," she returned sharply. "It is no concern of yours how the mistake was made. I simply wish you to return to me the package when I call again. Do you understand?"

"Understanding is not the issue here, madam," returned Holmes in an urbane tone. "Rather, it is a matter of proof. You will call again and expect me to hand over to you something I have received in the post. But how do I know you have any right to the object in question? For all I know, the brooch may have been stolen – possibly by you. If so, the rightful owner would scarcely thank me for handing it over to someone I have never met before and who refuses to give me her name."

Our visitor's face blanched perceptibly. "How dare you make such an impertinent remark!" she cried in a sharp tone. She appeared about to say more, but bit her lip and was silent for a moment, breathing very heavily. "I shall return tomorrow," she said at length, scarcely able to get the words out as her breast rose and fell with emotion, "and shall bring a pair of ear-rings with me that you will see exactly match the brooch." With that, she turned on her heel and left the room, slamming the door as she did so.

"What a very entertaining interview!" said Holmes after a moment.

"She appeared to be one used to having her instructions obeyed," I remarked, "but she also seemed very emotional about something."

Holmes nodded his head. "More than that," said he; "she is in a state of extreme anxiety. About what, I do not know – but I intend to find out. Of course, what she told us is a tissue of lies: There is nothing wrong with the clasp on the brooch, as I could see when I examined it."

"Will you follow her, to see where she goes?" I asked.

Holmes shook his head. "I am confident that the address on the reverse of that brown paper is pertinent to the matter. That is where I shall go."

He disappeared into his bedroom and did not emerge again for fifteen minutes. I looked up from the newspaper I was reading as he did so and received a shock. In the place of the neatly turned out fellow-lodger I had expected to see, there stood a disreputable-looking figure with a tangled beard, wearing an old, threadbare jacket and cap and a pair of ill-fitting corduroy trousers. The appearance was completed by a bright check muffler that was knotted round his neck.

"Is that you, Holmes?" I queried, not entirely in jest.

"Yes, Watson, it is I," returned he. "It is not only villains who can adopt disguises in order to pursue their ends. I am off to do a little research, and have adopted the character of Jack Brown, itinerant knife-grinder, which I believe will serve me the best."

"Knife-grinder?" I cried with a chuckle. "But you haven't got a grinding-wheel!"

"True, but that is not an insuperable obstacle. I have a small grindstone, at least," he continued, producing a cylindrically-shaped stone from an inside pocket. "That may suffice for my purposes. Now, I can't say when I shall be back, but I should be obliged if you would save me a little bread and cheese from your mid-day meal, as I may not have much opportunity to eat while I am out!"

With a little salute he was gone, and I was left to wonder what it was he intended to do. For a time I tried to distract my thoughts with the day's newspapers, but they contained little of interest and I soon found my thoughts returning once more to the strange business my companion was involved in.

It seemed likely to me that the brooch really did belong to our morning visitor, but as Holmes had remarked, it did not appear to be in need of repair. Why, then, had it been sent anywhere at all, and why, in particular, had it been sent to Holmes? Our visitor did not appear to have sent it herself, but how, then, did she know it had been sent to our address? Who had sent it and why? Did our visitor know who had sent it or not? Why was she so determined to withhold her own name?

One thing that seemed evident was that she did not want Holmes to learn anything of the facts surrounding the brooch, but Holmes, it was clear, was equally determined that he would uncover these facts. He had had a tiny message in the package he had received, pleading for his help, and he needed no further persuasion than that. As I was beginning to learn, it was only rarely that he refused his help when it was sincerely requested. This generosity of spirit put enormous demands upon his constitution, demands that would have quite exhausted another man, but which seemed only to spur my friend on to greater industry.

I should not wish my readers to think that I was excessively self-absorbed, but as I reflected on my fellow lodger's intense and energetic activity, I was led inevitably to a consideration of my own contrasting circumstances. Little more than a year had passed since I had been invalided home from the war in Afghanistan, and I had stepped onto the jetty at Portsmouth with my health seemingly ruined forever. That had, in truth, not proved to be the case: I was definitely in somewhat better health now than I had been twelve months previously; but the slightest over-exertion was still likely to reduce me to the state of a limp rag. In these circumstances, I had come to look to Sherlock Holmes and his work to provide the zest and interest in my life which I could not provide for myself. I had begun to keep notes of his cases and had on a few occasions been able to accompany him on his investigations, although that was not always possible. Now, as I pondered the mystery of the jet brooch, I found myself glancing frequently at the clock on the mantelpiece, wondering when my friend would return, and if he would have managed to learn anything of the matter.

It was the middle of the afternoon before I heard Holmes's characteristically rapid footsteps ascending the stair. I could see at once, from the expression on his face, as he burst into the room like a whirlwind, that he had had some success.

"The bread and cheese is on the table, under the cloth," I said.

"Good man!" said he. "I am famished! I shall just remove this beard, which has begun to irritate me, and be with you in a moment. Do you know if we have any beer in the house at present?"

"Yes," I said. "There are some bottles of pale ale in the cupboard. I'll open one for you."

A few minutes later, he returned from his bedroom. The beard had gone, along with the grimy jacket and cap, and he had donned his old dressing-gown once more.

"Now," said he, as he laid into his simple meal with gusto, "I dare say you are wondering what I have discovered."

"I have been able to think of little else."

Holmes laughed. "Yes, it is an intriguing little problem, is it not! You will be interested to know, then, that I have learned a great deal – although there are still one or two small points that are not clear to me.

"I made my way to Cumberland Gardens, in Kensington. It is a short, handsome street, with plane trees along the sides. The houses are very smart, all in white stucco, and clearly the homes of the wealthy. I began my investigation by simply loafing about there and striking up a conversation with anyone who seemed likely to respond. I make a grand loafer, Watson, even if I say so myself. It seems to come naturally to me. Gradually, through conversation with some of the ostlers in the nearby mews, a man delivering vegetables from his cart and numerous other people, I was able to accumulate information about the occupants of number eight. Needless to say, I also gathered information about the occupants of numbers two, four, six and ten, which I endeavoured to forget as soon as I had heard it.

"Head of the household at number eight is Sir George Datchett, who was one of the founders of the Sea Eagle Marine Insurance Company, and who was knighted just two months ago for his services to commerce. His wife is Lady Hilary Datchett, and from the description I was given of her, I am fairly certain it was she who called upon us this morning. The family is completed by a son, Michael, aged about twenty, who is up at Oxford but returned home for the Christmas vacation two weeks ago, and a daughter, Olivia, who is seventeen and in her final year at the Cheltenham Ladies' College. She returned home last week. The domestic staff at the Datchett household numbers four. There is a butler, who organizes the household, a cook, a kitchen-maid and a chambermaid.

"Having amassed this information, I abandoned my loafing about and called at the tradesman's entrance of number eight, where I offered my services as a knife-grinder. This was rejected, much as I had expected, but I did not give up.

"'My dear lady,' I said to the cook, who had answered the door to me. I was about to extol the benefits of having sharpened knives, but she interrupted me.

"'Don't you be so bold,' said she. '"Dear lady" indeed!' But she laughed nonetheless and I could see that by amusing her I had gained a small foothold. I thereupon offered to sharpen a pair of scissors for her free of charge, 'to demonstrate the worth of my technique' as I put it. This she assented to, in grudging fashion, and I had thereby gained a few more minutes of standing in the kitchen doorway, which was of course my aim.

"As I did my best to sharpen the scissors a little, I chatted with her and watched as she and the kitchen-maid – who appeared to be called Lily – bustled about their work. When I'd finished, I declared that it was 'thirsty work' and asked if I might have a cup of water, which she brought me. Up to that point, to speak frankly, I hadn't really learned anything very useful, but all at once things changed. Another girl came into the kitchen in a maid's uniform. She was there for only a few moments, picked something up and left again, but in that few moments I thought I might have found my way to the heart of the mystery. I was already fairly confident, if you recall, that the brooch and the request for help had been sent to me by someone who was young, female and a domestic servant. Neither the cook nor the kitchen-maid looked likely to be so imaginative or enterprising, and the butler could surely be ruled out. But in the few moments the other housemaid had been in the kitchen, she had glanced across to where I stood, in the doorway. For half a second, our eyes had met and in that half-second I had seen an unusual depth and intelligence in her eye. Surely, I thought, this was my mysterious correspondent! I might also add that she was quite attractive."

"I thought you always said," I interrupted, "that the appearance of your clients was a matter of complete indifference to you."

"Yes, of course, that is true when their appearance is irrelevant to the case, as it generally is; but there are odd occasions when a woman's appearance is not simply an irrelevant, peripheral matter, but a central feature of the case, and I found myself wondering if this might not be one such instance. Sometimes, a pretty face in a household or other group of people can have an effect akin to the tossing of a small pebble into a placid mill-pond: ripples are created which, although sometimes scarcely discernible, can reach a long way.

"'That girl who was in here just now,' I said to the cook as I sipped my cup of water: 'I believe I may know her. Is it not Susan, who used to be in the household of Lady Darlington?'

"'No, it ain't,' said the cook. 'It's Jane, who didn't use to be in anybody's household.'

"'Of course,' I said, 'but I do know her from somewhere. Is it Jane Robinson?'

"'No it ain't. It's Jane Page – and how would a shabby-looking fellow like you know someone as sweet as Jane?'

"I was saved from having to answer that question by the reappearance of the girl herself.

"'Here, Jane,' said the cook. 'This dirty-looking scoundrel reckons he knows you from somewhere. Do you know him?'

"The girl looked across the kitchen at me, a very dubious expression on her face. 'I don't think so,' she said.

"I glanced at the cook. She had turned away to put something in the sink, and I took the opportunity to take a card from my pocket and held it out so that the girl could see it.

"She took a step closer. 'You don't look like I thought you would,' she said in a doubtful tone.

"I leaned in at the kitchen door. The cook and the kitchen-maid were still occupied at the other side of the room. I dropped the rough accent I had assumed in my guise as a knife-grinder and, lowering my voice, I said 'I'm in disguise. I've come in answer to your request for help. Quickly! Tell me what has happened!'

"She came to the kitchen-door and stuck her head out so that she would not be heard by the others. 'That brooch–' she began.

"'Yes? Is it Lady Hilary's?'

"'Yes. Someone put it in my box.'

"'Where was that? At the foot of your bed?'

"'Yes. And then Lady Hilary found it was missing from her jewellery case, and asked me if I had seen it anywhere. I said I hadn't, but it was in my pocket. I was walking round all day with it in there, trying to think what to do with it. I couldn't tell her where I'd found it – she'd just think I'd stolen it. But I couldn't just put it back in her room, either, as she told me she'd looked all round there – on the dressing-table and on the floor underneath it. Then I thought of you. Mr. Boardman–'

"'Is that the butler?'

"'Yes. He'd read us out a report in the newspaper one evening of how Sherlock Holmes of Baker Street had solved some mysterious burglary when nobody else could, and I thought perhaps you could help me.'

"'I'll try. Who do you think might have put the brooch in your box? Are any of the other servants jealous of you?'

"'Oh, no,' she returned in surprise. 'We all get on famously. Hardly ever a cross word.'

"'Your master and mistress?' I asked: 'do they treat you well? Are you happy here?'

"'Oh, yes,' she replied quickly. 'It's like heaven. Sir George is the kindest man I've ever known.'

"'And Lady Hilary?' I asked as she paused.

"'She can be a bit sharp sometimes,' Jane replied, lowering her voice a little more, 'but I think she's quite nice underneath.'

"'The children?'

"'I never see much of Miss Olivia. She's been away at school all the autumn and only came home at the end of last week. She seems nice enough.'

"'And the son?' I asked as the girl hesitated.

"'He's very good-looking, and they tell me he's quite clever.'

"'But?'

"'He's a bit bold sometimes. One night last week, I think he'd had a little too much to drink and got a bit over-familiar with me, if you know what I mean. I told him it was wrong, but he wouldn't take 'no' for an answer and I had to push him away. I was worried after that that I'd get into trouble.'

"'When did you find the brooch in your box?'

"'Just yesterday morning. Then, about tea-time, Sir George gave me some letters to post for him. I put them on the hall table and went downstairs to get my hat and coat. While I was downstairs I had the idea of sending the brooch to you, so I put it in an old soap-box, filled it up with flour to stop it rattling about, and wrapped it up.'

"'Could anyone have learned where you sent it? Did anyone see you writing the address?'

"'No, I'm sure they didn't.'

"'Did you perhaps leave it somewhere unattended for a few moments?'

"'No – wait! – I did! When I got back up to the hall, I realised I'd not got my gloves, so I put the little packet on top of Sir George's letters and ran back downstairs to get them. It was only for a few seconds, though, and there was nobody about in the hall.'

"'But someone might have passed through the hall, and seen the packet lying there?'

"'I suppose so. But I didn't see anyone.'

"At that moment, the butler, Boardman, entered the kitchen and put an end to our discussion by asking what I wanted. I told him I was a knife-grinder, he said they didn't need any knives grinding and that was that. I thanked them for the water, gave the cup back to Jane, and wandered off.

"I then loitered near the end of the street for some time, sitting on a low wall, smoking my old clay pipe. I was just deciding what to do next when my mind was made up for me. The front door of the Datchett's house opened and out stepped a smart and fashionably-dressed young man who proceeded along the pavement, tapping his cane as he went. I followed him until I judged we were far enough from the house that our encounter would not be visible from there.

"'Excuse me,' I said.

"'No, I haven't got any small change that I can spare,' he responded, scarcely glancing in my direction, and evidently taking me for some sort of beggar.

"'I don't want any,' said I.

"'Then you should be very happy that I'm not going to give you any,' said he without breaking stride.

"I could see that the only way I could halt his progress long enough to speak to him would be to surprise him, so I again dropped my rough accent and in my ordinary voice simply said 'Michael Datchett?'

"He stopped abruptly and turned to me. 'Who the devil are you, and how do you know my name?' he demanded.

"'It is my business to know things,' I said, and gave him my card.

"'Well, Mr. Sherlock Holmes,' said he as he handed back my card, 'what is it you want?'

"'I am looking into a matter concerning Jane Page.'

"'What, Jane the housemaid?' he cried in surprise. 'What has she done?'

"'She hasn't done anything. On the contrary, things have been done to her.'

"'Such as?'

"'You have recently forced your unwanted attentions upon her.'

"'Oh, I see,' said Datchett. 'That is what she told you, is it? Well Mr. Sanctimonious Holmes, you don't want to believe everything you are told.'

"'Do you deny it?'

"'No. Why should I? What I dispute is the term 'unwanted.' The whole matter is, in any case, an utter trifle.'

"'And now someone has stolen something from the house and placed it among Miss Page's possessions, with the evident intention of getting her accused of theft and thus dismissed, or even charged with the matter in a court of law.'

"'Surely it is more likely, if anything is stolen, that she has stolen it herself.'

"'If so, she would hardly have told me about it.'

"'You might think that, but you can never tell what people might do. Look, if she's taken a silver teaspoon from a cutlery drawer in the kitchen, or whatever it is, just tell her to put it back where she found it and no one will be any the wiser. I certainly won't mention it to anyone. Now I really must be off.'

"He turned away, but I persisted. 'It would be natural to wonder if the attempt to incriminate her was a form of revenge, perhaps perpetrated by someone whose advances had been rebuffed.'

"'Revenge?' he repeated in an incredulous tone, then burst out laughing. 'Why on earth should I want dear Jane dismissed? Christmas is coming. In two or three days, there will be bunches of mistletoe hanging up, and then she will be obliged to accept a kiss from me. You can't go against the venerable traditions of antiquity, you know! You'll see – or, at least, she will!' With that, he turned away once more and I was left to ponder the matter further."

"With any result?" I asked.

My friend shook his head. "There are several possibilities," he replied, "with little in the way of evidence to indicate which is true."

"What will you do, then?"

"I really think I shall have to go round to the Datchetts' house this evening and try to force matters to a conclusion. If I don't, Lady Hilary will call here again tomorrow morning and I shall have to give her the brooch. She will then take it away with her and the mystery will remain unresolved. For all we know, Miss Page might then be dismissed from her position, and that is not something I can contemplate with equanimity."

Holmes fell silent then for several minutes, and it was apparent he was considering the matter from every different point of view. "Would you care to accompany me?" he asked abruptly.

I was somewhat taken aback by this sudden and surprising invitation. "I think I should like that," I replied, "if I would not be in your way."

"Not at all," said my friend. "I think it would be interesting for you to see what I hope will be the final act in this little drama. It will be best if we call when the family is all present, but before they sit down to dine, so be ready to leave just after six. Make yourself as neat as possible, Watson, and I will do the same. We must make a favourable initial impression or we may not be seen at all."

It was starting to snow as we took a cab from Baker Street, and as we rattled along through the dark, raw evening, the street lamps we passed served only to illuminate the whirling and tumbling snowflakes which filled the air. By the time we reached Kensington, just after half past six, I could see that the snow was beginning to settle.

The front door of the Datchetts' house was opened to us by a large and imposing-looking butler who took Holmes's card into a room on the left while we waited in the hall. A moment later the door opened and the butler re-emerged, followed by a pleasant-faced, grey-haired man of about fifty, who held Holmes's card in his hand.

"What is this about, gentlemen?" he enquired in a puzzled tone, as he closed the door behind him.

"Something odd has happened to a member of your household," replied Holmes, "and I have been trying to help. I am here to conclude the matter."

Datchett frowned. "Perhaps we should continue this discussion in the study," said he, indicating a door on the opposite side of the hall.

"Excuse me, Sir George, but are your family members all in the drawing-room?"

"Yes, they are, as it happens. We were just chatting, and are about to dine shortly. Why do you ask?"

"I think it would be better if I said what I have to say in front of everyone. It will not take very long."

"Who is principally concerned in the matter?"

"Your maid, Jane Page."

"Has she done something she shouldn't have?"

"No."

"Very well," said Datchett after a moment's hesitation, "if you think it best. But be aware that I am only agreeing to this because I have heard something of you, and your reputation is that of a gentleman. I do not want any unpleasantness. My wife detests anything of that sort, and my daughter is still a schoolgirl. Do you understand?"

Holmes nodded his head but did not reply, and, after a moment, Datchett opened the drawing-room door and we followed him into the room.

"This is Mr. Sherlock Holmes and his colleague, Dr. Watson," said Datchett, as his wife, son and daughter turned towards us, their features expressing surprise. "They have something to tell us. Go ahead, Mr. Holmes," he continued as he seated himself on a sofa.

"I will be as brief as possible," Holmes began. "Your maid, Jane, found a valuable piece of jewellery – a jet brooch – among her own possessions the other day, which she recognized as belonging to her mistress. She had no idea how it got there. Before she could do anything about it, Lady Hilary found that the brooch was missing.

Frightened that she would be accused of stealing it and unable to think what to do with it, Jane, on the spur of the moment, parcelled it up and sent it to me. This removed the immediate danger from her, by getting the brooch out of the house. No doubt she also thought that my involvement might lead to the truth being revealed.

"Unfortunately for her, Lady Hilary learned where she had sent the brooch. I assume, madam," he continued, addressing Lady Hilary, "that you saw the package lying on the hall table."

"That is correct. I happened to pass through the hall, and as I did so I glanced at some items on the table that were awaiting posting. Most of them, I could see, were letters my husband had written, but there was also a small package which appeared to have been addressed in a different hand. When I mentioned it to my husband later, he said he knew nothing about it."

"You then conjectured that it might have contained the brooch?"

"Yes, from the size and shape of the package."

"When you called at my chambers this morning, and gave me some rigmarole about the brooch needing repair, you did not assume I was involved in the theft of the brooch, or consider calling the police?"

"No, of course not. Like others, I have heard of you as one who solves crimes, not commits them."

"And yet you presumably felt sure by then that it was Jane who had sent the brooch to me."

"Yes. What of it?"

"Do you believe that Jane stole the brooch?"

"No."

"Why not?"

"Because I don't believe it is in her character to do such a thing."

"Well, if Jane did not place the brooch under her own pillow, then someone else did. She was led, understandably, to the conclusion that someone had deliberately tried to incriminate her, so she would be accused of theft and dismissed, a conclusion with which I entirely concur. If you did not believe that Jane had stolen it, you must surely have reached the same conclusion. There is no other possibility."

Lady Hilary hesitated a moment, and glanced at her husband as if for support, but the expression on his face was one of complete mystification, and it was evident she could receive no assistance from that quarter.

"I repeat," Holmes persisted, "if Jane did not remove the brooch from your jewellery-case, then someone else did, and I believe you know who that someone is, which is why you were so keen to hush the matter up, and had no intention of pressing charges against Jane."

"Oh, all right," said Lady Hilary abruptly in a sharp tone, rising to her feet. "I took the brooch myself. I was looking for a way of dismissing her. I felt my husband was becoming too fond of her, and that she was almost eclipsing his own children in his eyes."

"What nonsense!" cried her husband.

"But when I realised she had sent the brooch to you," Lady Hilary continued, ignoring the interruption, "I decided it had all got out of hand. I just wanted to get the brooch back, brush the whole business under the carpet and forget about it."

"So, let us be clear about it," said Holmes. "You yourself took the brooch from your jewellery case, and you yourself placed it under the pillow on Jane's bed?"

"Yes, I did. So now you know everything."

"Unfortunately, I do not."

"What do you mean?"

"Madam, you are not speaking the truth."

"How dare you call me a liar in my own house!"

"The house is irrelevant. I know you are not speaking the truth, madam, because you say it was you who placed the brooch under Jane's pillow, and I know you did not do so. I know you did not do so because no one did so: Jane did not find the brooch under her pillow, but in the box at the foot of her bed."

"It is no good, Mother," said Olivia Datchett, speaking for the first time since we had entered the room. "He has tricked you." She rose to her feet. "Mother is trying to protect me," she said, addressing Holmes, her voice breaking with emotion. "It was I who took the brooch, and I who placed it in Jane's box."

"Olivia!" cried her father. "Surely you would not stoop to such a low, mean trick!"

At this, the girl burst into tears. "It's true," she said, between sobs. "It was mean of me, and stupid, and I am very, very sorry."

I took a handkerchief from my pocket and passed it to her, as no one else seemed to be doing so, and she dabbed her eyes.

"Can this really be true, Hilary?" asked Datchett.

"Yes," replied his wife. "Olivia came to me and asked if I had seen the jet brooch recently, as she said she had been trying to find it and couldn't see it anywhere. But there had been an odd expression on her face as she spoke to me, and all the time I was looking for the brooch I suspected that she herself had had something to do with its disappearance. Eventually, in the evening, I confronted her with my suspicions and she admitted the truth. I then remembered the package I had seen on the hall table, and told her I was fairly certain I knew where the brooch had gone. I said I would try to get it back the next morning, so we could put the matter behind us and forget it had ever happened. Unfortunately, things did not work out so simply as that."

The room fell silent for a moment then, until, with a bewildered shake of the head, Datchett addressed his daughter. "Whatever can have possessed you, Olivia, to do such a thing? What has Jane ever done to cause you displeasure?"

"Mother told me in a letter that you have arranged for a special tutor to come in to coach Jane in English and arithmetic."

"And you were jealous of the attention? It is only one afternoon a week, Olivia – I am not sending her to the Cheltenham Ladies' College! She is an intelligent girl, and works very hard. I thought it was the least I could do. She has great potential and could make someone a good housekeeper one day – or a good wife."

"Then in Mother's last letter she said that Jane had been singing so beautifully that it had made you cry."

"Oh, that!" Lady Hilary interrupted. "I only put that in the letter to amuse you, Olivia. You know what Father is like; he cries when he hears sad songs; he cries when he sees a sad play; and sometimes he even cries when he sees a happy play! It is just his way, and I am sure we would not want him any different!"

"He never cries when I sing," said Olivia through her sobs.

"Ah! I see!" said her father in a tone of enlightenment. "Now I think I understand! Sit down, sit down, both of you – and you, too, gentlemen – and I will tell you something you do not know. Perhaps then you, too, will understand matters a little better." He closed his eyes for a few moments, as if gathering his thoughts, before continuing.

"When Jane was just a tiny baby," he began at length, "she was left at the foundling hospital. Neither she nor anyone else has any idea who her mother and father were. She was simply left one morning on the doorstep in a little wicker basket. A few months later, she was adopted by an elderly couple called Page from the East End, who gave her the name of Jane. The man worked as a cobbler, and apparently did all right for himself, but just a few years later both Mr. and Mr. Page fell ill and died within a few months of each other. Thus the only family little Jane had ever known had been taken from her. She was only five years old at the time. Mrs. Page's sister took her in for a little while, but she herself was elderly and could not cope with the child, and less than a year later she gave her up and she was placed in an orphanage. After a time, she was moved from that orphanage to another, and, later, to a third. In all, she remained in such institutions for nearly ten years.

"Two years ago, when we needed a new chambermaid, Jane was recommended to me. I agreed to take her almost as soon as we had met, for I could see at once that she showed great promise, and I have not been disappointed. Despite her unfortunate and unhappy childhood – which might have embittered or spoiled the character of some people – she has fitted into our household very well, and gets along well with everyone.

"Now I come to what occurred two weeks ago. I was in my bedroom early one evening, changing for dinner. My bedroom, as you know, overlooks the back garden, and through the window I could see that it was a dark, cold evening. All at once, as I stood before the mirror, buttoning my shirt, I heard someone singing in the garden below. I looked out, and there, illuminated by a light from the kitchen window, was Jane. She was putting some rubbish in the dustbin – not the most pleasant of jobs at the best of times – and singing softly and sweetly to herself. And do you know what she was singing, this girl who has never had any family, nor anywhere she could ever call her home? She was singing *Home, Sweet Home* – 'Mid pleasures and palaces though we may roam; be it ever so humble, there's no place like home.'

"As I stood there listening, I knew that the home she referred to was our house, that we had, without particularly intending it, given Jane the first real home she had ever had in her life. At that realisation, as much as at her voice, I admit I began to weep, but I am not ashamed of it. Your mother came into the room then, and asked me why I was crying. I told her I had been listening to Jane singing, but it was getting late, we had visitors coming, and there wasn't time for me to explain all the circumstances to her. There," said Datchett in conclusion, "that is the story of how Jane's singing brought me to tears, and I hope, Olivia, that you will understand the matter a little better now."

The room had fallen silent, save for the girl's quiet sobbing, and remained so for several minutes. Then Sherlock Holmes rose to his feet and took from his pocket the jet brooch, which he handed to Lady Hilary.

"That, I believe, concludes the matter, from my perspective at least," said he.

"Thank you for unravelling it all for us," said Sir George Datchett as he stood up and shook my companion by the hand.

We had turned to leave when there came a sharp pull at the front doorbell, and I heard the sound of singing from outside the house. A moment later, the butler entered the room to announce that the carol-singers from St Mary's had called, collecting for the parish charity.

"Oh!" cried Olivia. "I forgot it was tonight. I wanted to go with them! May I go? Please, Father? I can get a bite to eat later."

"Of course you may," said Datchett. "But you must wrap up warm, Olivia. It is a very cold night."

"And may I take Jane with me?" she asked. "I know from something she said to me this morning that she would dearly love to go carol-singing."

"Certainly, certainly," said Datchett, "but see that she, too, wraps up well. Now I must speak to the carol-singers."

With a cry of delight, the girl ran from the room, and I heard her footsteps clattering down the stair to the basement. We followed her father to the front door and stood for several minutes, listening to the carol-singers. Behind them in the cold night air the snow was now falling heavily. As they finished their carol, Datchett spoke to their leader, but I was distracted by the arrival behind me in the hall of two girls in overcoats, hats and mufflers. I turned to see them, but they slipped quickly past us and ran down the steps to join the carol-singers outside.

Presently, as the carol-singers made their way out of the gate and along the street, Sir George Datchett turned to us and thanked my friend again for his help. "Please send me your account for the trouble you have been put to," he said.

Holmes shook his head with a smile. "That won't be necessary," said he. "Sometimes the elucidation of the truth is itself more than adequate recompense."

As we made our way down the street, we came to where the carol-singers had stopped before another house, and paused a moment to listen. A girl at the back of the group glanced our way and I had an impression of a pair of bright, piercing eyes in a happy face, framed in tight dark curls. Holmes made a little gesture and she left the group and ran over to where we stood.

"I am confident everything will be all right now, Jane," said he, leaning over to speak closer to her.

"Yes," she returned in a breathless voice. "Miss Olivia has explained it all to me. It's all right now."

"But," he continued, "if at any time you find yourself in difficulty once more, do not hesitate to write to me again."

She nodded her head, then, raising herself on her tip-toes, she gave my companion a little peck on the cheek. "You look better without your beard," said she in a gay tone, and ran back to re-join the carol singers.

"I feel I should point out to you, Watson," said Holmes in a tone of embarrassment, as we resumed our progress down the street, "that that is not a regular occurrence at the conclusion of my cases."

I laughed. It amused me greatly to see my logical friend, usually so cold and unemotional, discomfited by a young girl, and I confess that I teased him about it for some time afterwards. Trivial incident though it may have been, I thought it worthy of mention here as being the only occasion in all of my records when my famous friend received payment from his client in the form of a kiss.

Also from MX Publishing

MX Publishing is the world's largest specialist Sherlock Holmes publisher, with over a hundred titles and fifty authors creating the latest in Sherlock Holmes fiction and non-fiction.

From traditional short stories and novels to travel guides and quiz books, MX Publishing cater for all Holmes fans.

The collection includes leading titles such as *Benedict Cumberbatch In Transition* and *The Norwood Author* which won the 2011 Howlett Award (Sherlock Holmes Book of the Year).

MX Publishing also has one of the largest communities of Holmes fans on Facebook with regular contributions from dozens of authors.

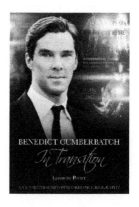

www.mxpublishing.com

Also from MX Publishing

Our bestselling books are our short story collections;

'Lost Stories of Sherlock Holmes' , 'The Outstanding Mysteries of Sherlock Holmes', The Papers of Sherlock Holmes Volume 1 and 2, 'Untold Adventures of Sherlock Holmes' (and the sequel 'Studies in Legacy) and 'Sherlock Holmes in Pursuit', 'The Cotswold Werewolf and Other Stories of Sherlock Holmes' – and many more......

www.mxpublishing.com

Also from MX Publishing

"Phil Growick's, 'The Secret Journal of Dr Watson', is an adventure which takes place in the latter part of Holmes and Watson's lives. They are entrusted by HM Government (although not officially) and the King no less to undertake a rescue mission to save the Romanovs, Russia's Royal family from a grisly end at the hand of the Bolsheviks. There is a wealth of detail in the story but not so much as would detract us from the enjoyment of the story. Espionage, counter-espionage, the ace of spies himself, double-agents, double-crossers...all these flit across the pages in a realistic and exciting way. All the characters are extremely well-drawn and Mr Growick, most importantly, does not falter with a very good ear for Holmesian dialogue indeed. Highly recommended. A five-star effort."
The Baker Street Society

 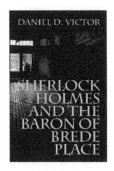 

Also from MX Publishing

The Detective and The Woman Series

The Detective and The Woman
The Detective, The Woman and The Winking Tree
The Detective, The Woman and The Silent Hive

"The book is entertaining, puzzling and a lot of fun. I believe the author has hit on the only type of long-term relationship possible for Sherlock Holmes and Irene Adler. The details of the narrative only add force to the romantic defects we expect in both of them and their growth and development are truly marvelous to watch. This is not a love story. Instead, it is a coming-of-age tale starring two of our favorite characters."
Philip K Jones

www.mxpublishing.com

Also from MX Publishing

The Sherlock Holmes and Enoch Hale Series

 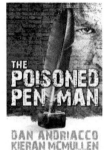 

The Amateur Executioner
The Poisoned Penman
The Egyptian Curse

"The Amateur Executioner: Enoch Hale Meets Sherlock Holmes", the first collaboration between Dan Andriacco and Kieran McMullen, concerns the possibility of a Fenian attack in London. Hale, a native Bostonian, is a reporter for London's Central News Syndicate - where, in 1920, Horace Harker is still a familiar figure, though far from revered. "The Amateur Executioner" takes us into an ambiguous and murky world where right and wrong aren't always distinguishable. I look forward to reading more about Enoch Hale."
Sherlock Holmes Society of London

www.mxpublishing.com

Lightning Source UK Ltd.
Milton Keynes UK
UKHW011540290620
365747UK00016B/482